VERA'S STORY

Escape to Freedom

J. K. DEROSA

CHATHAM HOUSE

Chatham House, LLC
Concord, MA

To Vera Caslavsky

A Remarkable Woman

Note to Reader

"To be ignorant of what occurred before you were born is to remain always a child." —Cicero

This book is based on a true story.

Just before Vera Caslavsky left the US to travel back her native Czechoslovakia, she sat down for 5 days and 5 nights to write a brief monograph. She titled it "25 Years of Exile," with an introduction she named, "I Am Going Home."

She wrote it to give to family and friends who may never have learned what really happened. She also hoped her grandchildren would be interested in the struggle that brought her and them their freedom.

I was deeply moved by her story and wrote this book based on the monograph and many hours of conversations with Vera. The backdrop of her story spans an era from the first president of an independent Czechoslovakia through Nazi occupation and Soviet domination, to modern times after the fall of the Berlin Wall. But the story is about people, not politics. Although I filled in monograph and memory gaps, I doggedly retained the emotional content she conveyed to me. In that regard, it is an "almost true" story.

Because it is such a deeply personal story, I wrote it in first person—through her eyes. It stands as the powerful tale of a family caught up in the storm of history. It is a story of courage, hope, and perseverance. A human story. Vera's Story.

Czech People in Czech Lands

BOHEMIA   MORAVIA   SLOVAKIA

6th Century–1918. Czech Lands of Bohemia & Moravia existed along with Slovakia for centuries and were part of the Austro-Hungarian Empire until the end of WWI.

CZECHOSLOVAKIA

1918–1935. After WWI, Czechoslovakia existed as a prosperous parliamentary democracy in central Europe.

NAZI GERMANY

1938–45. Czechoslovakia was occupied by Nazi Germany and became Protectorates of Bohemia, Moravia and Slovakia.

SOVIET UNION

1948–89. Czechoslovakia was reconstituted by Russian liberators but soon after came under Soviet Control.

CZECH   SLOVAK

1989–93. The "Velvet Revolution" freed Czechoslovakia from Soviet Control. It peacefully split into the Czech and Slovak Republics.

Chapter One

GET-AWAY VACATION

O ur plan was to escape to the West.

In June 1965, our family of three was allowed to take a vacation in Yugoslavia. At the time, Jarda and I were both in our early 30s and we had been married for 12 years. We lived in Prague and worked for the Czechoslovak Mining Institute. Our daughter, Veronika, was 8 years old.

Although I had resigned my position as a town meeting member in Prague, citing the work load of my PhD studies and motherhood, I had done it in such a way as to remain in good standing with the Communist Party. I had recently come to harbor anti-Communist sentiment, whereas Jarda had always felt that way. Only the closest of friends knew of our current discontent with the government. No one knew of our intentions.

In those days, Yugoslavia was a country lying along the Adriatic coast from Greece in the south to Italy in the north. In more recent times, just as Czechoslovakia split into the Czech and Slovak Republics, Yugoslavia splintered into Slovenia, Croatia, Bosnia-Herzegovina, Serbia, Montenegro, and Kosovo—not peacefully, but after a bloody war—and Yugoslavia no longer exists.

But then it was considered a friendly socialist country, and we were able to obtain consent from our local Communist Party head for the vacation trip. Our passports allowed us to travel from Prague through Hungary to the coast of Yugoslavia, all countries within Soviet control.

We rented a room from an elderly couple in a Yugoslav fishing village near the Italian border. Our landlords were friendly people, but we were afraid to seek their advice or confide in them. The Party kept dossiers on everyone. We couldn't trust that they wouldn't report us, and they couldn't trust that we weren't testing their loyalty. We all carried with us the constant fear of betrayal.

Each day, we went for a swim at a beautiful beach about 10 km south of Trieste, Italy. Because the prices in Yugoslavia were low, this beach was also visited by many Italians. If we could make it across the border to Trieste, we would be free.

Veronika played in the sand with a little Italian girl, and she was not bothered by the language barrier. We were able to converse with the girl's mother in English. She had a kindness about her that inspired trust. After several days, we decided to risk our confidence with her. Maria was sympathetic and promised to seek advice on our behalf from her brother, a policeman in Trieste.

That afternoon, Jarda went to explore the coast, looking for a place to cross into Italy on foot. He sauntered casually in the direction of Trieste dressed in a swim suit, pretending to be collecting shells. He thought he may have actually crossed into Italy but couldn't be sure because the border was not well marked. He didn't want to attract attention by asking anyone.

On his way back, he met Yugoslav soldiers patrolling with

dogs. He ignored them, sauntering along, picking up shells as he went. They paid no attention to him, apparently considering him to be one of the locals. But it was clear the border was patrolled.

The following day, we met Maria on the beach again. She told us crossing the border was risky because smugglers were active in the area and border guards fired on them without regard to whose territory they happened to be in.

She made us a kind and unexpected offer. She said she would come the next day without her daughter and travel home with Veronika in place of her daughter. When we managed to get out of Yugoslavia, we could pick up Veronika at her house.

But what if we didn't get out? Could we leave Veronika with a stranger whose language she didn't even speak? We could not.

We began to look for other ways to escape. The water there was warm, and Jarda and I were both good distance swimmers. If we placed Veronika on a rubber float at night, we could swim across the bay into Italian waters.

We watched the bay that night. Heavy ship traffic moved in and out of the channel all night long. If we were in the water, they would not be able to see us, and we would be too slow to get out of their way. Swimming across the bay was too dangerous.

We couldn't walk across the border. We couldn't leave our daughter with strangers. We couldn't swim to freedom. We began feeling desperate.

A number of foreign tourists on yachts were anchored near the beach. What would happen if we approached them and told them of our plight? We studied them. They seemed self-absorbed and aloof. What if they didn't want to be bothered with our problems? Would they turn us in to authorities? Not only would that prevent our escape, it also would have dire consequences when we were returned home. We decided that risk was too great.

After a few days, we decided on a new approach. Taking leave of our landlords, we boarded a train to the Slovenian Alps. We knew the train closely followed the Yugoslav-Italian border. Perhaps there was someplace along the way where we could dash undetected to freedom.

Unfortunately, we found the entire border sealed with a barbed-wire fence patrolled by guards with dogs. Between the village stops, guards were spaced about 500 meters apart. Once we passed a guard, we might have been able to toss Veronika from the slow-moving train to people on the Italian side of the fence, but we couldn't be sure we had enough time—or enough ability—to jump across before the next group of guards spotted us.

The train continued north and turned west along the Austrian border. After the war, Austria had become an independent state. They had self-declared to be permanently neutral in the Cold War. If we made it there, we would also be free.

We decided to get off at the Kranjska Gora station. The tiny village sat nestled in the Alps, just south of Austria. Large signs prohibiting entry onto all roads and paths leading to Austria told us exactly what direction we would need to head. Nowhere did we see any patrols. It would be difficult, maybe treacherous, to walk through the Alps to freedom, but we were up for the challenge.

We got a room to wait for nightfall, but that afternoon, fate dealt us another blow. Heavy snow began to fall. We watched the storm rage all night.

The next morning was bitter cold. It was clear that crossing the Alps on foot would now be impossible. Travel by means other than rail would be impossible for days, and our approved vacation time was nearing its end. We had no other option than to leave on the first train out.

Hungry, cold, and tired, we bought a large loaf of rye bread just before we boarded. It was fresh enough that it warmed my hands and I hugged the bag close to my chest. I could feel the warmth rise to my chin and I could smell the aroma of caraway seeds and sourdough. We ate the entire loaf. It warmed our insides, comforted and replenished us. We made one last desperate plan.

The train would travel through Ljubljana, at that time the capital of the Yugoslav province of Davra Banovina, which lay due south of Prague on a straight line through Austria. Once there, we would go to the Austrian consulate and argue that we had to return to Prague via the most direct route possible— through Austria. If they granted us the transit visa, we would simply get off the train once we were in Austria.

When we arrived at the Austrian embassy, we tried to convince them it was the only way we could get home before our allotted vacation time was up. It didn't seem to matter to them. I don't know whether they believed us or whether they suspected we intended to escape, but either way they said no simply because it was not their role to grant such a request. We were living in a time and a place where no one would take chances.

Now we had exhausted all possibilities of escape. At least, that's what we thought.

That night, we boarded a train that would take us home as specified in our passports. The circuitous route went from Yugoslavia, east to Hungary, north to Slovakia, then northwest to Prague. Never would we be outside the borders of a socialist state.

Our small compartment had no other passengers. Jarda stored the luggage overhead and sat across from me. Veronika's little body leaned up against mine. I put my arm around her, and she quickly fell asleep with her head on my lap and her legs curled up on the seat next to her. We settled in for the long trip home.

Giving in to sleep meant giving up on escape. Yet, we had exhausted all plans to get away. Hadn't we already given up? After all, we were on a train back to Prague, back to our lives as "loyal citizens of the Czech Socialist Republic." The train was returning us to where every part of our lives was controlled and scrutinized.

Still, the instinct to escape haunted me. Although I was extremely tired, the momentum of the last two weeks favored constant vigilance. I drifted in and out of sleep. I saw Jarda doing the same. Veronika slept soundly as children do.

Suddenly, the train stopped. I opened my eyes and glanced at my watch. It was midnight. I heard voices outside. Jarda looked out the window and tried to assess what was happening. We didn't know it, but the same unpredictable Alpine weather that had prevented our escape from Yugoslavia into Austria just two nights before had flooded the tracks in Hungary. Our train had been diverted through Austria!

When Jarda figured it out, he turned to me and shouted, "Take Veronika and run! We are in Austria! Run!"

My mind was racing so fast I found it difficult to comprehend what he was saying.

The train lurched slowly forward.

Jarda made a move toward the door of our compartment. He turned and saw I was struggling to wake Veronika. "Hurry," he said.

I coaxed Veronika to her feet and wrapped a blanket around her. I could see she had fear in her eyes. I placed my hands on either side of her head and kissed her saying, "It's all right. Come. We have to go."

Jarda grasped the handle of the door and reached up to grab a small suitcase. I remember thinking it wasn't the one I would have chosen.

As we dashed down the aisle of the train, I pictured myself jumping to freedom with Veronika in my arms—much as an olympic athlete mentally rehearses a gymnastic move before performing it. But Jarda stopped short at the exit door. He looked back at us, the color drained from his face. I could see the despair in his eyes. The train had picked up too much speed for us to jump off.

It was our last chance at freedom. We'd missed it!

Chapter Two

MÁ VLAST

From the 6th Century On: Czech people in Czech Lands

The decision to escape was a difficult one for us. Yet, we felt it was the only option. Like most Czech people, we were filled with an independent spirit, but we were also connected to the land of our ancestors. Freedom compelled us forward, while nostalgia called us back.

As a little girl I walked in the woods with my grandparents and swam in a local pond with my father. As a teenager, I often traveled by train to meet Jarda in a nearby town, where we walked and talked for hours by a great river. As a young couple, we lived in the magnificent city of Prague where we raised Veronika.

Most people feel an affinity to the country in which they grew to adulthood. The feelings I have for the Czech lands and people are very deep—and they are inextricably entwined with history.

What do Americans know of the complicated history of

central Europe? "We eat small children for breakfast." That was my response to my Harvard-educated friend who once used the word "barbarians" to describe the people of the Czech Republic. Although I didn't take offense, she realized from my reaction that "barbarians" was not a good word choice. It became a standing joke between us. Whenever either one of us said something dumb, the other would say, "Yes, small children for breakfast."

In all fairness, Europeans seldom know the names of more than a few of the states in the US. They often mix up the city of New York with the state of New York, and don't actually know its capital is Albany.

Like most Americans, my friend knew enough to know that in ancient times, kingdoms came and went, and in modern times, wars and atrocities spanned the continent. The names of the countries and the borders themselves had been defined and re-defined by conquerors, liberators and freedom fighters.

History, they say, is written by the victors. Since the Czech people were not always the victors, our true history is a combination of what is written in books and what is etched in our hearts. To understand the Czech heart, you must know something of our true history.

That history goes as far back as the 6th century when we migrated into central Europe from Slavic lands to the east. Although political boundaries have changed, Czech people trace their families back many generations in that same land. It's been my experience that it is the people who define a country, not the political boundaries.

In the 6th century, we organized ourselves into state-like entities, until we formed the Great Moravian Kingdom, and later the Kingdom of Bohemia. Even today, Czech people in the western part of the Czech Republic sometimes refer to themselves as Bohemian, while those in the east call themselves Moravian. In legends it is told that the Czech name derived from an early Slavic tribe in central Bohemia known as the *Čechové*.

We existed as an independent state within the Holy Roman Empire, and over the centuries developed our own language, literature and art—even our own alphabet, which fit the writing of Slavic languages better than did the Greek alphabet.

When my grandparents were born, Bohemia and Moravia were under the regime of the Habsburg Emperor Franz Joseph, who reigned longer than any other European monarch, and whose rule spanned fifty-million subjects—German, Italian, Hungarian and Czech. Even with conflicting tensions and attempted revolutions, his power and prestige held together the Austrian Empire, of which the Czech lands were a major part. Under his rule, the economy was booming and a middle class rose.

THE CZECH PEOPLE REMAINED FIERCELY INDEPENDENT, AS they had for centuries and Franz Joseph gave them some autonomy. They kept Czech as their official language in government and established a Czech-speaking section in Prague's Charles University—against the wishes of the Germans.

At the end of World War I, the Austrian empire collapsed and the Czech lands of Bohemia and Moravia were combined with those of Slovakia to form the new country of Czechoslovakia. After Hitler invaded Czechoslovakia and subtracted some lands, he renamed what was left the Protectorates of Bohemia, Moravia, and Slovakia.

At the end of World War II, the Russian liberators restored Czechoslovakia, but soon became occupiers who installed a socialist state. With the fall of the iron curtain, we split from Slovakia and became simply the Czech Republic.

. . .

THE CZECH PEOPLE I KNEW GROWING UP HAD ANCESTORS who migrated from the east twelve or thirteen centuries before. They were still speaking their own language, living their own culture, and inhabiting their own lands. Whether they lived in the east or the west territories, whether they themselves or their occupiers called them Bohemian or Moravian, whether they were part of a larger Czechoslovakia or not, Czech people thought of themselves—and still think of themselves—as Czech.

Those lands hold a special place in the heart of the Czech people. The enchanting little towns and villages are like nowhere else in the world. The people celebrate with festivals. Mighty rivers flow across the rural countryside and through the major cities. In Prague, the presidential palace and the St. Vitus cathedral sit on a high hill above the River Moldau (*Vltava* in Czech), looking out over a vast panorama.

It is as difficult for me to describe the beauty of this land as it is to describe the character of its people. When I want to evoke the feelings of serenity and pride in my country, I listen to a symphony by the Czech composer Bedřich Smetana called *Má Vlast,* that is translated into English as "My Homeland."

I close my eyes and picture the landscapes of my native land and relive its rich history. I see Prague's grand castle where the earliest Czech royalty resided. I hear the sounds of the great Bohemian rivers, as well as the war cries of Maiden Warriors from an old Czech legend. I ride along with all the warriors who have defended our homeland or sought our independence. For me, the wind once again passes over the fields and whistles through the forests. I drink and laugh at village festivals.

Listen to Má Vlast.
Close your eyes.
See what I see,
hear what I hear—
this magnificent land,
the cadence of independence
that defines its people.
Now you know the Czech heart.

Vera Caslavsky
Spring 1990

Chapter Three

LIFE BEFORE THE WARS

1876–1912: My Grandparents' Generation

The Czech lands and culture that had existed for centuries is the world into which my grandparents were born. The life they led is the life my parents expected to lead. It was the life I and my family were supposed to lead. It was the life we were meant to pass on to our children. It was the life before the wars.

My paternal grandfather, Vilem Novak, was born in 1876 and lived most of his life in the enchanting eastern Bohemian town of Chrudim. About 100 kilometers to the west lies the magnificent city of Prague. Although Grandpa Novak gained a classical education in an advanced secondary school—called a *Gymnázium*—his family did not have enough money to enroll him at the university in Prague.

Resigned to starting his adult life in Chrudim, my grandfather and his girlfriend made plans to marry. Unfortunately, she became ill with tuberculosis. They married and lived happily for a brief period before she succumbed to her disease.

Her father was a successful farmer. Grateful for the few years of happiness his daughter had in her brief marriage, he rewarded his son-in-law by enabling him to realize a lifelong dream. He paid my grandfather's way through law school.

Shortly before getting his law degree, Grandpa Novak and his best friend placed an ad in the paper stating that two young men were seeking girlfriends in their 20s. From the many replies they received, they selected two sisters named Weisbauer from Vosice, a village near Chrudim.

One of the sisters, Lida (Ludmila), had studied piano at the conservatory of music in Prague. Two of Grandpa Novak's life-long passions were theater and music. She and Grandpa fell in love and eventually got married.

Her father was the principal of an elementary school in Vosice. When he learned of his future son-in-law's love for the violin, he told him about a three-quarter size violin made in 1805. The instrument was lying idle in the school attic. That violin had been used by the previous principal to teach his own son how to play. That young boy, František Skroup, went on to become the famous Czech composer who wrote *"Kde Domov Muj,"* (Where My Home Is), the Czech National Anthem.

Grandpa Novak became an accomplished violinist by practicing on that violin. It was one of his most prized possessions, and in later years, I often listened to him play. When I was six years old, he taught me to play on that same violin. Before Grandpa Novak died in 1945, he bequeathed the violin to me, and it stands as an important artifact in my family's story.

MY MATERNAL GRANDFATHER, EDUARD KUDRNKA, WAS born to very poor parents in Koci, a charming little village about six kilometers east of Chrudim. His father was a bricklayer, but also an alcoholic. His mother had to assume the burden for both childrearing and providing for the family.

Grandpa Kudrnka also attended the *Gymnázium* in Chrudim. In order to save his shoes, he walked there barefoot, carrying his shoes and putting them on when he arrived in town. At his mother's urging, he entered the seminary in Hradec Kralove, 100 kilometers east of Prague. He was eventually ordained a Roman Catholic priest.

Assigned to a parish near Jičín in northeastern Bohemia, he got in trouble with the church hierarchy. He was somewhat of a rebel. He criticized them for participating in politics and pursuing luxuries while neglecting the poor.

At some point, a young girl came to the parish to work. She was there to assist her aunt in cooking for the residents. She and Grandpa Kudrnka eventually fell in love. He was subsequently excommunicated from the church. They married and moved to Prague, where he studied medicine.

In a lot of ways, he lived a life similar to the 15th century Master, Jan Hus, a preacher, university professor and a catholic priest who tried to reform the Catholic Church prior to Luther. Hus called for a renewal of ethics among the clergy. He asked them to submit themselves to only one authority—the authority of conscience. He demanded the clergy become a community of Christians, not just in name, but foremost in their hearts.

Hus became a hero of the Czech people when he refused to recant and was burned at the stake. Although the followers of Hus did not prevail, his credo "Truth will prevail!" decorates the presidential flag. His statue dominates the Old Town square. July 6th, the day of his death, is commemorated as a national holiday.

Grandpa Kudrnka followed the philosophy of Jan Hus. He graduated from the prestigious Charles University just before the outbreak of World War I. With his religious and medical background, he matured into a philosopher and humanitarian who cared for people, especially for the poor.

Even though he was no longer a priest, Grandpa Kudrnka believed in God in his thoughtful, private way, and in the principles advocated by Jan Hus. He enjoyed the respect of the community. He opposed the use of drugs and alcohol, and overindulgence in meals and luxuries. He studied the use of herbs in medicine and preferred the natural ways of healing.

Both sets of grandparents grew up in charming little towns in Bohemia. They found love and married. They considered themselves to be part of the long tradition of a free and cultured people. My grandfathers had good educations through the *Gymnázium* system and the great universities in and around Prague. They expected their children, my parents, to grow up and prosper in the same way.

Then came the wars.

Chapter Four

THE UNLUCKY GENERATION

1914–1989: My Parents' Generation

My father was seven years old and my mother just two when a Serbian nationalist assassinated Archduke Franz Ferdinand of Austria. Within weeks, war broke out all around them. World War I raged on for four more years, engulfing Europe in one of the deadliest conflicts in modern history. Over 15 million people died.

My parents were never afforded the opportunity for a happy and carefree childhood. My father was old enough to internalize that something really bad was happening. My mother was too young to realize there had ever been better times. She became a sullen and gloomy child. For her, life was simply filled with death, destruction, fear, and scarcity.

My grandparents were nearly 40 years old when the war broke out. They were certainly affected by it, but they were already set in their ways. They had already known a better life and had expectations it would someday return. Grandpa Novak continued doing legal work in Chrudim. Grandpa Kudrnka practiced medicine. He was sent to Vysoke nad Jizerou near the Polish-German border to head up a military hospital, seeing to the care and recuperation of wounded soldiers.

Hope for a better life did return after the war ended in 1918. My mother's family moved to Chrudim where my father's family lived. The Allies dissolved the Austro-Hungarian Empire and established the free, democratic republic of Czechoslovakia. This consisted primarily of the lands of Bohemia, Moravia, and Slovakia, and was a multi-ethnic state with about half the citizens Czech, the other half Slovak and German in equal proportions.

Grandpa Kudrnka bought a house with four apartments. He and Grandma Kudrnka lived in one apartment with their daughter Vera (my mother) and her little brother Eda, and Grandpa set up a medical practice with an examination room, waiting room, and study in the other apartments.

A university professor named Tomáš Masaryk became the first president of the new state. As an outspoken philosopher of Czech origin, he embraced many of Hus's teachings advocating truth. His motto was "Do not fear and do not steal," (*Nebát se a nekrást*). Over the next 20 years, Czechoslovakia developed into a prosperous industrial country with a strong agricultural base.

For my parents, growing up with hope for a better life was a new and unfamiliar feeling. If they embraced the prosperity of the times and the freedom of living in a democratic government, this was to be short-lived. Problems were brewing on the horizon.

The ethnic Germans who lived in the northern region of the new state did not like being under Czech rule. Likewise, old conflicts surfaced between the Czechs in the west and the Slovaks in the east. The times were hopeful but tumultuous.

Still carrying the scars of war, my parents—Vilem Novak and

Vera Kudrnka—became young adults. Both were well-educated at the *Gymnázium* in Chrudim. Father was a handsome, quiet young man, with a dry, English-like sense of humor. Mother had a pleasant face and a slight build. She was thought to be one of the prettiest girls in town. They met and fell in love.

Like most young people, Vilem Novak and Vera Kudrnka had their hopes and dreams. My father was studying law as his father had before him, and my mother was flourishing in her education at the *Gymnázium.*

When the Great Depression of 1929 began, people living in the United States and Europe plunged into poverty and despair. Many lost all hope for the future. By the time an economic recovery took hold in 1933, Hitler and the Nazi Party had risen to power in Germany.

As the economic recovery began, my mother graduated from the *Gymnázium* program with honors. She then spent a year in a school for young women in Annecy, France. She always recalled that time of her life fondly. She was planning to spend one more year in England, but while she was home visiting her family and her boyfriend, I was conceived. So she married my father instead.

To my father, this was a welcomed turn of events because my mother was his one great love. My mother, however, felt she had been pushed into marriage too early—before she was ready for it. She added the burden of that belief to her melancholy child-hood, and this affected her outlook on life.

My father opened a law practice in Chrudim, and tried to make life better for my mother. He moved them into the upstairs apartment in Grandpa Kudrnka's house, where I was born. But the psychological scars of my mother's childhood, combined with the disappointment of her early pregnancy and marriage, were too much for her to overcome. She had already set her course for a lifetime of sadness and regret.

Many of the citizens of German descent who lived in the western regions of Czechoslovakia near the northern German border openly supported Hitler. They requested an annexation of this so-called *Sudetenland* to Germany. In 1938, despite protests by the Czechoslovak government, England and France signed the Munich Agreement with Hitler and handed over the *Sudetenland* to Germany. The Czech people felt they had been betrayed by the West.

Appeasement did not satiate Hitler's appetite for what he called "living space" for the German people, nor did it prevent the outbreak of another world war. From his vantage point in the *Sudetenland*, Hitler was able to invade Czechoslovakia. He divided the country into the Protectorates of Bohemia and Moravia, and a puppet Slavic State. Then he invaded Poland and, shortly after that, World War II began.

This was the first time my mother's emotional state became critical. She collapsed and was treated for several months at a clinic in Prague. My father had to recruit Grandma Kudrnka's maid, Fanynka, to help with my care.

The Nazi occupation lasted from 1939 to 1945, and during this time many citizens of Czechoslovakia were imprisoned and sent to concentrations camps from which they did not return. Most of the Czechoslovak Jews who did not get out before the invasion were killed.

When the war finally ended in 1945, my parents were well into their 30s. They welcomed the Russian liberators and the re-establishment of Czechoslovakia. However, by time they turned 40, the Communists had seized power and the country was under the control of the Soviet Union. The Cold War erected an "Iron Curtain" that divided East from West in Europe.

My parents had exchanged Nazi jailers for Soviet ones. The Cold War continued for over four decades.

My grandparents had tasted freedom before the wars. Their generation was able to grow up and start their families in relative peace. My children and I came to know freedom after them. My generation lived long enough to see the Berlin Wall come down and democracy return to the Czech Republic.

But my parents lived most of their lives suffering the effects of worldwide political and economic crises. As children they lived through WWI, as young adults they lived through the Depression followed by WWII and the Nazi occupation. Liberation by the Russians brought a brief period of freedom, only to be ended by a Communist takeover and Soviet domination.

My father didn't live long enough to see the Berlin wall come down, and my mother was in her late 70s when that happened. Vilem Novak and Vera Kudrnka Novak were part of the unlucky generation.

Chapter Five

FAMILY

1934–39: My Pre-School Years

I was born on January 18, 1934, in Chrudim, the same enchanting and historical town in eastern Bohemia as my grandfather before me. I was born with my loving grand-parents around me. I was born to a father who read me stories at night and to a mother who lamented my birth and never embraced motherhood with delight. I was born in a free and democratic Czechoslovakia.

My christening took place in the magnificent gothic Church of the Assumption of the Most Blessed Virgin Mary (*Kostel Nanebevzetí Panny Marie*).

My father's father was well-established in Chrudim as a professor of law at the School of Agriculture. Grandpa Novak had a nice house with a large garden, and he participated in the town's civic affairs, directed amateur plays in the town theater, and was concert master in the local symphony orchestra. I remember him as a kind, rotund gentleman who was drawn to spiritualism. He often told me ghost stories. In retrospect, I see that they were fantasies, and he was just putting me on. Grandpa was a quiet and reserved man, but a great jester with his family and close friends.

My mother's father, as a well-respected medical doctor, was much more outgoing. Grandpa Kudrnka would seldom walk through the town without greeting a number of neighbors. He was especially good to those who could not afford to go to the doctor. He not only gave them free medical care, but oftentimes he gave them money. Bread and soup were served to all comers every Friday. He stood straight and tall in stature as well as goodness.

I WAS FOUR YEARS OLD WHEN ENGLAND AND FRANCE signed the Munich Agreement surrendering the *Sudetenland* to Hitler. The seeds of disaster were sown by that single act. It would end 20 years of a free and democratic Czechoslovakia. When I was five years old, the Nazi *Wehrmacht* rolled into Prague.

The president of Czechoslovakia, Edvard Beneš, fled to the west and formed a government in exile. Nazi Germany took control of every aspect of government in my homeland. Prosperity ended. Hope died, and the one burgeoning democracy in central Europe was dissolved. The Czech people were at the disposition of Hitler's whims. I no longer lived in Czechoslovakia. I now lived in the Protectorate of Bohemia, and once again the world was at war.

I don't remember hearing tanks roll into Chrudim, or seeing soldiers. What I do remember is how the mood in my house changed. My grandparents seemed worried all the time. My father was more preoccupied. My mother was increasingly more uneasy—until the worst thing that could happen to a five-year-old happened. My mother went away.

When she collapsed, the household was thrown into a panic. She was sent to a clinic in Prague, and I had no idea if or when she would return. For several months my care was in the hands of my father, my grandparents, and our dear maid Fanynka.

I don't have a lot of memories of how my mother treated me before her institutionalization. I know she wasn't happy with the way her life unfolded, that marriage and motherhood had come too soon. I think she blamed my father for that. I don't know if she resented me too, or if she resented my relationship with Fanynka or my grandparents. Maybe my father's close relationship with his mother bothered her. I don't know. What I do know is that after she returned things were difficult.

Then they got worse.

My mother's brother, my uncle Eda, was studying to become a doctor at Charles University in Prague. He expected to practice medicine like his father, Grandpa Kudrnka. Despite the Nazi occupation, life would go on. However, the ancient feud between the Germans and the Czechs reared its ugly head at Charles University.

The university was established in the 14th century by King Charles IV, who also wrote laws for governing the country, built several gothic architectural landmarks and supported development of the arts and culture overall. However, in the 15th century, the House of Habsburg married into the lineage of King Charles IV, and eventually a Habsburg became Emperor of Bohemia. That lasted until the 19th century when the Czech lands came under the rule of the wider Habsburg Austro-Hungarian Empire.

Since the time of Emperor Franz Joseph, Charles University

had been split into German and Czech sections. Each section retained its own language and traditions. One day the Nazis closed the Czech portion of the University. I think at the same time they closed many of the Czech institutions of higher education.

So Uncle Eda was ousted just before graduation. Instead of returning home as he was instructed to do, he and a friend managed to escape from the occupied lands, first to Yugoslavia, then to France. There they joined the retreating French army. They finally ended up in Great Britain, where they became members of the Czechoslovak unit of the British army. Uncle Eda finished up his degree at Oxford and became a physician in his military troop.

But Uncle Eda was not the only Czech youth who escaped Nazi control. Many sons and daughters could not be accounted for. To punish their parents, the Nazis set up a detention camp in Svatoborice in southern Moravia, about 200 kilometers from Chrudim. It wasn't a concentration camp in the usual sense, but the prisoners were fenced in and kept under the control of their Nazi captors. Grandpa and Grandma Kudrnka were sent there as punishment for their son's presumed escape from Nazi control.

Grandpa was able to work in the camp as a physician to the inmates, but he was given no special privileges. He was separated from Grandma while they lived in the camp. On one occasion when he caught sight of her outside, he called her over to the fence and gave her a kiss through the barbed wire.

For the "crime" of that kiss, they were locked up in the ice-cold morgue. Grandma was released that evening, but Grandpa was kept there all night. He later told us that, to survive the cold, he walked in circles in the small room all night long. The next day, both of my grandparents were transferred to the German prison at Brno-Kounice, where inmates were often tortured.

With the disappearance of her brother and the imprisonment of her parents, my mother's condition worsened. Without my grandparents in the house, it was like living in a black hole with no sensory perception. I merely survived.

Chapter Six

LIVING OUR LIVES

1939–1944:
My Grammar School Days Under Nazi Occupation

Eventually, my grandparents returned home. It could have been after a year or only a few months. I have no sense of it. During their absence, it was my father who ensured the family's survival. For the most part, my mother was incapable of helping.

Once my grandparents returned home, we might have been able to resume a somewhat normal life—except my mother's mental health did not allow for that. She was now severely affected. In the years I attended elementary school, she left many times for stays at a mental hospital. I don't remember how many times she went there or for how long she was gone. The truth was, she had already left me emotionally. The larger truth is I had felt the absence of my grandparents more severely than that of my mother.

Every time Mother returned home, her illness made our relations even more complicated. She would often say things that hurt the ones she loved. She would complain about me and my behavior for hours. She seemed to give the most trouble to the ones she professed to love the most. As a result, I became a difficult child for her to raise.

I do not remember having conflicts with my father, Fanynka, or either of my grandparents. In fact, Grandpa Kudrnka often reassured me that I was a good girl when I cried on his lap after one of the numerous scoldings I received from my mother.

My father took me to art shows during the day and read Kipling's stories to me at night. He bought me a small bicycle and on weekends or after work we would ride to a nearby pond to go swimming or fishing. The pond belonged to a farmer my father had once represented in court. We had the whole place to ourselves. Those times alone with my father are among my most precious memories. To this day, I swim every day and think of our time together at the pond.

Fanynka was also very special to me. She was special to all of us. She was only 16 when she came to the family as Grandma's maid. Her father had lost his farm because of his drinking and gambling. Our relationship with Fanynka was based on mutual love, respect, and loyalty. She took care of me at those times when my mother was ill, hugging and shyly kissing me good night. She was constantly there for all of us, and she was selfless.

Fanynka cooked three meals daily per the instructions of Grandma. Grandpa grumbled at that, saying he was satisfied with coffee and bread for breakfast as well as supper, but it was clear that he too loved Fanynka. She raised chickens, geese, and rabbits in our courtyard so we would have enough meat, eggs, and lard. Fanynka and I would cut grass or glean ears of grain which she used to feed the animals.

Grandpa compensated Fanynka well enough to ensure her

independence in her old age. But it turned out she didn't need that because she stayed with us until she died in her late 70s. Oddly enough, she died in my mother's arms.

The support I received from my four grandparents was very important to me. Although we lived with my Kudrnka grandparents, I could easily walk to my Novak grandparents' home a few blocks away. The care I received from Grandpa Kudrnka was unforgettable. He was a source of understanding, love, and support. Every day after school, he would take a break from his practice to give me a hug. Later, he sat next to me while I did my homework.

Every day at around 5 o'clock he invited Grandma for a walk. When I was old enough, they often brought me along. We were accompanied by their dog Aficek. We walked along the fields and forests that surrounded Chrudim. Grandpa felt most relaxed in communion with nature, and I inherited that trait from him.

Grandpa Novak was a member of the Blackbird's Nest, a men's club whose members were the town's most prominent citizens. They met once a month for dinner. They each wore a cap tipped with a bell and meetings were called to order with an Easter rattle. Dinner was followed by a period of levity, during which anything or anyone was game and liable to be "roasted."

Even in dark times, Grandpa and the Blackbirds had a sense of humor. On his 65th birthday, the Blackbirds coached me to recite a little rhyme for Grandpa. I was 6 at the time. The little poem began: "The Lily of the Field grows for a long time, but Dill longer" ("*Konvalinka dlouho roste ale kopr dele*"). However, if you hesitate as you say this so *kopr dele* sounds like *ko prdele*, it's meaning changes to: "The Lily of the Field grows for a long time, but what the f- - -."

They all had a good laugh when I recited that, which of

course I didn't understand at the time. But I do remember Grandpa's 65th birthday like it was yesterday. I remember the fun, food, drink and festivities. It ended with a walnut tree being planted in Grandpa's honor in our garden.

Grandma Novak was a very private person, gentle and kind. A special bond existed between my father and his mother. Her affection for him got passed down to me and I, in turn, loved her very much.

One time I found her cleaning out her chest of drawers and burning some correspondence. She looked at me with tears in her eyes and told me not to forget to cultivate bonds with my cousins. She said as one grows older, one becomes very lonely in life. It's funny, you don't realize the wisdom in your grandmother's words until you are already a grandmother yourself.

She also gave me one of her pins made with Czech garnets. Garnet is my birthstone and ruby red my favorite color. Whenever I see a garnet, I think of Grandma Novak.

Each Christmas Eve, both of my grandparents would come to dinner at our apartment. The decorated Christmas tree was hidden behind a closed bedroom door. Later in the evening, the door was opened to show the lit candles shining in the dark and the presents for everyone sitting under the tree.

During the after-dinner festivities, my mother and grandfather Novak played the piano and violin together and we all sang Christmas carols. We also took part in many traditional superstitions. One was to crack open apples to see the pattern in the flesh, revealing a star or a cross at the core. The cross signified illness or bad luck, while the star signified good luck or longevity. We each floated a walnut shell with a candle in it in a basin of water. Depending on whether the candle went out or reached the "shore" at the edge of the basin, that would determine our destiny. If your shell sailed in a different direction from the others, that meant you would be leaving home the following year.

At 11 PM, the family would go to midnight mass at the church where I was baptized and would later celebrate my marriage.

Even though five Christmases went by while the Nazis occupied Czechoslovakia, for me the war didn't mean soldiers or battles or death and destruction. One time I heard air raid sirens as airplanes flew overhead on the way to bomb a factory in a neighboring town. But for the most part, I saw the war through the lens of my family's distress, although they attempted to shield me from it.

Maybe my mother's temperament reflected the war, but I perceived it as an illness, a family matter, and a personal misfortune. I was in the constant company of my grandparents, my father, and Fanynka. Despite the war and my family's troubles, I successfully finished four years of elementary school.

I know now that during that time, many of our citizens were imprisoned or sent to concentration camps from which they never returned. The Jewish population was all but wiped out. But none of that was visible to a little girl growing up in Chrudim. Then again, much of what happened was not visible to the rest of the world either.

War is one of the world's great tragedies. People suffer unspeakable fates. That was true for the Czech people under Nazi rule. But I didn't know about any of that. In my little world, there was only one great tragedy. At the age of 69, following a surgery, Grandpa Novak died. I was 10 years old.

In his will, my grandfather bequeathed the 1805 violin to me. His most prized possession became my most prized possession.

Chapter Seven

RUSSIAN LIBERATORS

1944–48:
Becoming a Teenager as Russian Liberation
Turned to Soviet Domination

Because my grades were good, I was inducted into the Czech competitive *Gymnázium* program in 1944. I finished one year there when the war ended.

I was 11 years old when the Germany-dominated Protectorates of Bohemia and Moravia were liberated by the Russians. We were afraid of the Russians because we didn't know much about them, but we welcomed them because they got rid of the oppressive Nazis.

A dozen troops were stationed in our garden. They used our telephone connections and my mother offered them food. She even housed one Russian officer and his family in our home. I have photos of myself playing with his daughter, who was my age. I remember her singing Russian songs.

. . .

THE RUSSIANS HELPED THE COUNTRY RECONSTITUTE OUR Czechoslovak government. President Beneš returned home from exile and established a democratic government. He appointed Jan Masaryk, the son of the former president, as the minister of foreign affairs. The new government consisted of a coalition of leading parties. One of those was the Communist Party.

Some people worried that the Russian strangers in our country were becoming an occupying force. This was born out in my schoolwork. I was in my second year of the *Gymnázium* program, studying Latin and the classics. The political realities of the times were reflected in the curriculum.

In my first year there, I was required to learn German, the language of our occupiers. In my second year there, I was required to learn Russian, the language of our liberators.

1946 (12 years old)

ALTHOUGH THERE WERE POLITICAL BATTLES GOING ON IN the democratic government, these were relatively happy times. The new government restarted a Czech youth organization called the Sokol which the Protectorate government had previously shut down. Sokol advocated a "strong mind and a strong body."

Lectures, discussions, gymnastics, and outings provided physical, moral, and intellectual training for the nation's youth. My father became an organizer, so it afforded me the opportunity to interact with other youth at events.

I also went to dances, ice skated in the winter and swam in the summer. My parents and grandparents were living a relatively happy life, and I was living the life of a normal pre-teen.

❦

1947 (13 years old)

UNFORTUNATELY, MY FATHER BECAME ILL WITH SEVERE headaches and deteriorating eyesight. When the symptoms worsened, he sought medical help. The diagnosis was a shock to all of us. He had a tumor in his brain. During surgery to remove the tumor, he died.

I lost the most important man in the world to me. My childhood ended that day. My mother was a wreck. But the bad news did not end there.

Right after my father's death, Mother told me she was pregnant. If her first pregnancy was too soon, this one was too late. She didn't have the will to raise another child, especially with her husband gone. She wanted to abort the fetus, but she left the decision to me.

Of course, this wasn't fair—I was still a child. I knew of her depression and mental illness, however, and I feared what would happen if she had another child. So I said yes.

I made that decision during a period of deep grief following my father's death. I also made the decision based on consideration of my mother's well-being. But for the rest of my life, I would return in my mind to that fateful day and wish I had said no. Saying no would have given me a brother or sister to confide in as the years passed. *No* would have meant that I might have a sibling to comfort me in my elder years. *No* would have meant I might have comforted a sibling.

With the Soviets worshipped as liberators and with their physical presence in our country, the Communist Party had the support of a fair number of Czech citizens. After years of Nazi persecution, the socialist promises of equality, work for all, no homelessness, and free medical care sounded good to many people.

Beneš still maintained the Czech spirit of freedom and independence. Masaryk, with his American-born wife Charlotte, acted as a counterforce to the Communist influence.

I was always good in school, but after my father's death, I dedicated myself even more so to my work—probably as a way of covering the hurt. I had a teacher named Mr. Šada who was attentive to the needs of all the kids. They gave him the title "Dad." In the absence of my father, he paid particular attention to me, and I flourished in my studies at the *Gymnázium*.

☙❧

1948 (14 years old)

AS TIME WENT ON, THE COMMUNISTS STEADILY INCREASED their power, in spite of the fact that their popular support was diminishing. Soviet Russia became the prime ally and confidant of the Communist regime in Czechoslovakia. Just after I turned 14, there was an election slated, one in which the Communists feared they would be thrown out. So the Communists initiated a government overthrow.

At that time, President Beneš was quite old, weak, and sick. He offered little resistance. A few days after the overthrow, Jan Masaryk was found dead on the floor of the courtyard of the ministry, presumably the victim of murder or forced suicide. The circumstances of his death were never made public.

My carefree childhood had come to an end with the death of my father. Similarly, post-war Czechoslovakia's democracy ended while still in its childhood. My country and I were destined to mature under a Communist dictatorship. In ways we could never have predicted, the character of the Czech people would be changed. I would be changed.

A child and a people changed by war and politics.

Chapter Eight

EQUALITY FOR ALL

1949–1952:
My High School Years; the Communists Tighten their Grip

Soon after the Communist takeover of the government, we were informed the western border with Germany and the southern border with Austria were cordoned off with barbed wire and fortified with minefields. Observation towers were built at regular intervals and the entire no-man's land was guarded by soldiers with dogs.

The propaganda machine claimed the fortifications were necessary in order to deal with the threat posed by western European countries in general and the US in particular. The truth was they were more afraid of their own people escaping than a foreign military force invading. No threats were identified at the borders with east Germany to the north, Poland to the northeast, the Ukraine to the west, and Hungary to the south-east, because these countries were already firmly under Soviet control.

We were exposed to a barrage of propaganda. Everywhere you turned, you saw the communist promise of equality for all—the duty and dignity of work, no homelessness, and free medical care—over and over again. In rural Chrudim where work, homelessness, and medical care were not problematic, we weren't being affected by the new communist policies. However, as time went on we heard that in the larger cities, communist rule was radically altering the Czech lifestyle.

Work for all meant everyone was assigned a job, whether it was one they wanted or not, and whether they were needed on the job or not. Since the workplaces were no longer private enterprises, few cared.

No homelessness translated into the state confiscating property and assigning everyone to a home. When there weren't enough homes, they stacked multiple families together in one residence. Oftentimes this was a residence that one of the families had previously owned and occupied by themselves.

Free healthcare meant doctors were often paid the same as plumbers. While plumbers could work under the table, doctors needed to practice in a state-run medical facility. Therefore, the supply of new doctors decreased at the same time that the promise of free healthcare sent demand through the roof.

The loyal party members became powerful implementers of this "equality for all." Soon, the best way to find good housing, secure the job you wanted, or get the chance to see a doctor was to trade favors with these privileged bureaucrats. Permission was almost impossible to obtain without something to offer in return. Corruption became rampant, and an underground economy sprung up.

In many places in Czechoslovakia, goods and services became scarce. The middle-class standard of living disappeared. Many who worked harder to achieve more were viewed with suspicion. The best way to survive was to become a loyal party member. The price you had to pay was to report to the Communist Party the activities of other members. Those who were deemed loyal, that is, those who informed on their fellow citizens, were given positions of authority. Those who were deemed disloyal were punished.

Branding someone as disloyal became a ready outlet for petty jealousies as well as a tool for settling old scores. Disloyal workers fell to the bottom of the social order. Disloyal professors lost their teaching positions. Children of disloyal families were barred from higher education and good jobs.

The risk of pushing back against the system or even complaining about how you had been treated was very high. Politically unreliable people ended up in prison. Openly anti-communists simply disappeared or were found dead.

I continued to study hard and flourish at the *Gymnázium*. Communist youth groups were formed with ballroom dance lessons once or twice a week. About 40 percent of my class favored Sokol over the Communist groups, because Sokol had historically leaned toward the policies of Jan Masaryk. But to pad our resumes and appear compliant, we joined the communist youth groups and went to their dances. But we danced to the music, not to the Communist tune.

I was hovering near the top of my class as graduation approached. My mother and grandparents continued to live as best they could and according to their values. Grandpa Kudrnka did everything he could to make life easier for the poor and downtrodden in post-war Communist Czechoslovakia. That gave him special insight into a great deal of private information about his patients. Sometimes a woman who had more children than she could care for would come to him looking for an abortion, and sometimes Grandpa would perform it, keeping the procedure secret. The local Communist Party bosses continually pressured him to report any anomalies he may have observed. Because he wouldn't do it, he was deemed a suspicious person in their eyes and placed under surveillance.

One day he was performing an abortion and the police raided his office. Grandma was assisting him and managed to toss the instruments before the police could gather evidence against him.

The Communist Party had little moral objection to abortion, which had been legal in Russia for many years before the war. It was only Stalin's worries about low population growth after the war that made abortion illegal. The Communists used that illegality as the excuse to arrest Grandpa for his lack of cooperation. He was seventy-two at the time.

⚜

1951 (17 years old)

GRANDPA KUDRNKA WENT TO JAIL AND FORMAL CHARGES were filed against him. Because he was so loved by the people in the town, no judge in Chrudim would try him. Grandpa was transferred to the town of Holice 15 miles away.

We received several nice letters from him during his imprisonment. He seemed in good spirits, and we were all hopeful that, without physical evidence, he would be freed. We hoped this would happen before my upcoming graduation from the *Gymnázium* program.

I had already been accepted to continue my studies at the prestigious Charles University Medical School in Prague.

46

Grandpa was very proud that I was following in his footsteps, as Uncle Eda had done before me.

※

1952 (18 years old)

THE WEEK OF MY GRADUATION, WE GOT WORD GRANDPA had committed suicide in prison. The authorities said Grandpa wanted to spare us the humiliation of the trial and the confiscation of our house for his crimes. The local undertaker who brought his body home told us privately there were signs of severe beatings.

The clergyman who presided over the funeral avoided a graveside eulogy. He said it was because of the crime Grandpa was accused of, but we were sure the priest feared prosecution. Still, the large number of people who came to the funeral was a testament to what a good man he had been.

The task of delivering Grandpa's eulogy fell to my mother. With great difficulty, she wrote it, but in keeping with our family dynamic, I had to step in and deliver it for her.

My grandfather was buried in the family grave in the cemetery of the Church of the Holy Cross in Chrudim. The grave is a simple one, without insignia. It now contains the remains of the family I grew up with in Chrudim—my Kudrnka grandparents, my parents, Fanynka, and my uncle Eda.

Our family was torn apart during the war. The politics of the times took a toll on my parents' relationship. They suffered a great deal. My mother's life never got to a happy place. My father never got the happy marriage he deserved with the woman of his dreams.

My *Gymnázium* years were bracketed by two great tragedies.

At 15, I lost my father and at 18, I lost Grandpa Kudrnka. Even though I was shielded from many of the consequences of the war and the atrocities of our occupiers, I was aware of the fragile nature of life under communist rule. Fortunately, one chance event brought me happiness and set the course for the rest of my life.

Chapter Nine

JARDA

1949–1952:
The Good Part of my High School Years

At my father's funeral, his older sister Eva invited me to come spend my Christmas break with her. Aunt Eva and I were always close, and I welcomed the chance to get away from all the sadness in our house. When the time came, I took the train to Liberec, which is about 100 miles north of Chrudim. She met me at the station and we had a tearful but happy reunion.

She cooked for me and talked to me the way Fanynka and my father had. I felt very much at home with her. Also, there were lots of sights to see in Liberec, a large industrial town near the German and Polish borders. Liberec had some of the best technical schools in the country, schools known for their production of fine glass and for glass research. Shops around town had displays of the beautiful Bohemian crystal popular for hundreds of years all over Europe.

Aunt Eva was very social. One night each week, she welcomed a small group from the town to play bridge at her house. A handsome young man named Jaroslav Caslavsky was among the players. I was immediately attracted to him, and thought, or maybe hoped, he had paid a little more attention to me than would be normal. I was 15, going on 16. He was 20. His nickname was Jarda.

He carried himself well and was very intelligent. He worked at the Glass Research Institute in Liberec. I found out he was from Hradec Králové, just north of Chrudim. At the age of 17, when the war ended, he left home to study chemistry at the Technical High School in Liberec.

On the last night of the card game before I was to return to Chrudim, Jarda asked if he could write to me. I said yes. Later, Aunt Eva sat me down for her wise counsel.

"I can see you like Jarda," she said.

"Yes," I said, somewhat embarrassed. I was not used to romantic involvement with boys.

"Well, he is a very nice young man, intelligent, handsome. But there is a problem."

"Yes," I said, "I know. He is an outspoken opponent of the Communist Party. But none of our family likes the —"

"That's not it," she said. "Everyone knows he's involved with a married woman here in Liberec. There's nothing wrong with being attracted to a handsome and intelligent young man, but you have to be careful of that one."

Careful was not the first thing that came to my mind. Besides, what harm would there be in a letter? And he lived and worked in Liberec, 100 miles away from me. I was still in high school. I had a hundred excuses why there was no need for me to be careful.

After returning to Chrudim, I waited, but no letter came

from Jarda. I assumed he was no longer interested in me. What I didn't know was that Aunt Eva was looking out for my wellbeing. Eventually, she told me Jarda was indeed interested in me, but she made sure that before he wrote me a letter, he broke up with his married friend.

Jarda and I started corresponding by mail. At first the letters were just friendly. He asked me about myself and I learned about him. He was active in Sokol and very athletic. An accomplished Alpine skier, he was especially good at slalom and had won some competitions. His spare time was filled with everything from sports to cards. He hated the Communists and was not above making fun of them. I thought that showed he had courage.

After a while, his letters began including his romantic thoughts about me. That wasn't a problem for me. I was already in love with him. By the end of our first year of exchanging letters, Jarda professed his love for me. I was now 17 and had one more year of *Gymnázium.*

What he did next warmed my heart.

Although he still worked 100 miles away in Liberec, the Glass Research Institute had its head office in Hradec Králové, just 20 miles from Chrudim. Jarda applied for a transfer, which he received. The reason he gave me for making the move was he wanted to be nearer to me. I couldn't imagine someone as wonderful as he was would change his life for me.

We were now a manageable distance from one another.

After school each day, I took the train north about 7 miles to the thriving industrial city of Pardubice. Jarda traveled south about 15 miles to meet me. We walked along the grassy banks of the River Labe that ran through the city and planned our life together. It was there we first made love.

Sometimes on the weekends, we went 60 miles north to Sněžka Mountain in the Krkonoše range on the border between the Czech Republic and Poland. The summit is the highest point in the Czech Republic and the views are spectacular. In the winter we went there to ski. Some parts were too steep for me, but Jarda skied all the slopes. Sněžka Mountain was one of his favorite places.

He eventually confided in me at that time that he had another reason for leaving Liberec. His anti-Communist stance there had proven dangerous. One night, he had been awakened by a telephone call from his high school teacher and Sokol brother, Mr. V—

"Wake up, Jarda! You must come to school this instant. I need you to help me with something!"

Mr. V— needed Jarda to make a microfilm of some documents and photographs which verified that one of the leading Czech Communists had worked for the Nazis as a "*capo*" while a prisoner in at the Sachsenhausen concentration camp. This man was now a highly-placed government functionary, but he had been present during the torture and execution of political prisoners. He later became prime minister and president of Communist Czechoslovakia. His war record was hot information, and was intended for delivery to Dr. Milada Horakova, a leading anti-Communist activist.

The Communists feared Horakova, and soon after takeover they imprisoned her and accused her of treason. She was sentenced in a mock trial and executed. Mr. V— was also arrested and sentenced to hard labor in the uranium mines, where he was murdered in a staged accident.

Mr. V— did not betray Jarda's involvement in releasing the documents, but the police were aware of their relationship. So Jarda was interrogated several times. On one occasion, the police led him down a corridor where an open door revealed a nude woman being tortured by thugs. Jarda was sure they wanted him to see this in order to intimidate him, but he continued to act as if he had nothing to do with anything disloyal.

From the questioning, Jarda could tell they knew some young man had assisted Mr. V— with the microfilm. They asked Jarda if he knew a certain person in Liberec. Jarda did know him, but said he didn't. The other man closely resembled Jarda in appearance. It was clear the police were trying to figure out whether the accomplice had been Jarda or this other person. They must have been convinced it was not Jarda because they released him, or maybe they just figured they could pick him up again later. The truth was both Jarda and the other young man were anti-Communists.

When they released Jarda, he found the other man right way and warned him of the police's intention. Together, they executed a plan for his look-alike to escape from the country. Dutch truck drivers carrying goods from Prague to Holland smuggled him out of the country in the false bottom of their truck. When the police showed up at the look-alike's home and workplace, they couldn't find him. This took some of the pressure off Jarda.

When Jarda later inquired about using the Dutch route for his own escape, however, he found it was no longer available. The route had been discovered and was gone forever. His life and mine would have been very different if he had escaped Communist-ruled Czechoslovakia at that time.

I assumed his move to Hradec Králové would mark an end to his troubles with the Communists. Years later, I would find that I was mistaken.

He and I shared moral values. We believed in honesty. We cared for others and valued family. Neither of us trusted politics. We both had independent spirits. We made our own observations and came to our own conclusions. This was not consistent with the communist government running Czechoslovakia. We both had a deep love for our country and held out hope that someday it would return to a democratic state.

Although I had been shielded from many of the atrocities committed by the Nazis during the war and by the Communists afterward, I knew there was some risk in marrying Jarda. At the time, however, I didn't think much about it. I was young and in love.

The one difference between us was this: I was willing to work with the Communist Party to make the lives of the Czech people better, but Jarda was not. At the time, this didn't seem important because neither of us was involved in politics. However, the Communist Party kept dossiers on everyone. It was the civic duty of every citizen to report on the words and actions of co-workers and neighbors, even family members. I would've been expected to report on Jarda.

Jarda's dossier must have noted his anti-Communist senti-ment. Maybe the incident with Mr. V— added to that or maybe this was all they had on him. We didn't know. What we did know was even though he was brilliant and had a real knack for chemistry, he was prohibited from attending college.

They were watching him.

With my father, Grandpa Novak, and Grandpa Kudrnka all gone, I wanted to marry Jarda as soon as I graduated. Since I had been accepted to Charles University and since Jarda was under suspicion with the authorities, we decided to move to Prague. I would go to medical school and he would find a job. Hopefully, he would be anonymous in the big city.

Chapter Ten

PRAGUE

1952:
We Begin Married Life on Our Side of the Iron Curtain

Grandma Novak's sister lived in Prague, and she let us move into her basement. Jarda soon got an unremarkable job outside his field of chemistry. But we had little money and he was willing to do any work that would support us.

Convinced that Jarda had an intellect superior to mine, and to most of the students I knew, I hatched a plan. I changed my major to Chemistry in an effort to get him into the Chemistry department, either as a student or a research assistant. So I entered Charles University as a Chemistry major instead of as a medical student.

I got a part time job with a very kind professor in the Geology department doing work in minerology. My task was to draw maps of the places where particular mineral deposits could be found throughout Europe.

Because the university lab was in the heart of Prague, Jarda picked me up every day after work. He was much more sociable than me and chatted with my boss every time he came by.

One day, the professor asked me, "Why isn't that smart young man of yours continuing his education?"

I told him. "Because of a misunderstanding from years ago, the Party won't let him."

The professor said, "Let me see what I can do."

Shortly thereafter, Jarda was admitted to the Geology department of Charles University. Once he was in and doing well, he was able to change his major to Chemistry. My plan had worked. Now we were both majoring in Chemistry at one of the finest universities in Europe.

On December 20, 1952 we were married in a government office in Prague. We travelled to Chrudim at Christmastime and again got married on Christmas day in the Church of the Assumption of the Most Blessed Virgin Mary, where I had been christened. Our married life together had begun.

The early days of our marriage took place within the backdrop of Communist rule in the Czech Republic. Once the Communists had succeeded in overthrowing the government 4 years before, they suppressed freedom and democracy and installed a dictatorship controlled by the police and military.

If Jarda's anti-Communist sentiments became known in Prague, he would again become a marked man. We couldn't be sure he wasn't already. We tried to disappear into the masses in Prague and be careful not to offend anyone in the Communist Party. So for several years we kept to ourselves, spending all our time at college, work, and home.

As we neared graduation in 1956, Jarda and I got involved in an exchange program with students from the Technical University in Dresden. Whenever the German students arrived in

Prague, we were expected to show them around. We enjoyed our interaction with them and made a number of friends. We toured the country together, going as far away as the High Tatra mountains in Slovakia. When we later traveled to their school in East Germany, we toured by bus all the way to the North Sea. One of our stops was Berlin.

At that time, Berlin was divided into the Russian, British, and American zones. However, the zones were not yet separated by a wall, and passage between sectors was possible. The secret policeman in charge of our bus warned us that, should anyone flee to the western sectors, there would be immediate consequences which would result in the immediate expulsion of a German student, and maybe an end to the exchange program altogether.

Jarda and I gave a lot of thought to the idea of fleeing to the west. An escape meant we would betray our fellow students and the German exchange students with whom we had become friendly. It also meant we would fail to get our degrees from Charles University only a year before graduation. For these reasons, we decided to stay with the tour and return home. If we were to escape, we would do so at a more opportune time.

After graduation, we both decided to continue on for our master's degree. Unfortunately, Jarda's dossier was brought up and he was refused any further education. That confirmed for us that he was still a marked man, and it underlined the necessity of a future escape.

I was pregnant, and we didn't make a fuss. Jarda got a job at the Mining Institute, and I entered graduate school. I also worked part time in the Mining Institute.

In 1957, our daughter Veronika was born. A year later, I was awarded my master's degree and went to work fulltime for the Mining Institute. I continued with my schooling at night, studying for my PhD. Our lives were very busy and devoid of politics.

We had a friend in Prague. Franta and his wife were members of the Communist Party. One time, Franta dropped in on us for a chat and a cup of coffee. We sat in the kitchen and talked politics. He was a good enough friend that we didn't fear he would report our discussion to anyone.

When we complained about the Communist Party, he said, "Look, if only opportunists, careerists, and blockheads are going to govern us, we can hardly expect any change for the better, can we?"

Jarda responded by saying that Communist ideology was similar to Nazism and that nothing good would ever come of it. Although their political philosophies were quite different, our experiences under Nazi occupation was identical to those we experienced under Communist rule.

However, I had some sympathy for Franta's argument. If people other than the Party *apparatchiks* were involved in public policy, maybe things would get better. So, when a leading Communist at the Mining Institute, came to me in 1959 to ask permission to put my name on an election ballot, I agreed. If elected, I would become a Town Meeting Member in the 9th district in Prague.

I had been persuaded by Franta's comments. Now I had to tell Jarda.

Chapter Eleven

THE SEEDS OF DISCONTENT

1959:
I am Elected Town Meeting Member while
Party Bosses Run the City

What had been an insignificant difference between us before we were married became a major issue after. There was the devil to pay at home for my decision to let my name be put on the ballot. Since opposition names weren't allowed, once my name was placed, my election was assured. Jarda and I engaged in seemingly endless arguments that continued into the wee hours of the morning.

Jarda felt I was deserting the principles he stood for by agreeing to support and cooperate with an evil regime. I tried to convince him that since we were stuck there, I could try to make life better for us, as well as for others. We could find no common ground. To this day, Veronika, who was then barely 3 years old, recalls overhearing us argue, and she remembers how frightened she was.

Jarda finally stopped opposing my decision, although he remained convinced it was wrong. In his mind, I had betrayed his dearly held ideals.

I was elected to represent our neighborhood at town meetings and to participate in a health commission overseeing the district nurseries and kindergartens. The neighborhood was also supervised by a "Citizens Committee" run by local Communists. Even though I was not a party member, I was obliged to attend this committee's meetings.

When I arrived for my first Citizen's Committee meeting, I avoided using the Communist greeting, "Honor to work!" Instead, I used the miners' greeting, "Honor to God!" This infuriated the woman in charge of the committee. If it had not been for an older Communist gentleman who came to my defense, my career in politics might have ended right then.

Another member of the committee did not like me. Even though she was the mother of one of my co-workers at the Mining Institute, she secretly complained about me to a higher party committee and told my husband she had done so. Maybe she assumed a good Communist husband would straighten out his wayward Communist wife. She was the only one we knew who complained, but there may have been others. The regime liked to set people against each other to spread rumors and generate distrust and fear. The common belief was that every 20th person in the country was on the payroll of the Communist secret police. People jockeyed for those positions.

I made an honest effort to deal with problems of the nurseries and kindergartens in our town district. I listened to staff and parents, and I discussed ways to improve the quality of care and wellbeing of the children. After several months of work, I presented a report with recommendations to the committee and was commended for it. I felt exonerated.

Months went by and nothing changed in the district. A year later, the new edition of the guidelines for kindergartens and nurseries was released. I was anxious to see my recommendations in the document. They were not there and the document turned out to be nothing more than a reprint of the old one. Not a single recommendation I had made was implemented.

I won't say I was disillusioned. It's more like my eyes were opened.

The centralized power was not interested in my recommendations, regardless of their merit. Jarda had been right. He told me I had been selected for my post as window dressing. The Party wanted people who were not Party members to seem involved in government—especially young women. I had been used for propaganda. Franta and I were wrong, and my husband was right.

This awakening was a rude one for me. I went to the Secretary of the Party at the district Communist bureau to hand in my resignation. For all practical purposes, this man ran the town. I was careful not to criticize the Party. Instead, I said the stress of fulltime employment, caring for a small child, and studying for a PhD was affecting my health. He tried to persuade me to retain my town meeting membership, but when I broke down in tears he agreed to let me go.

One day I came home from work and asked Jarda if we could talk. We sat quietly together as I told him he was right about the Communist Party and public policy. I said I needed to apologize. I also told him that, as far as I was concerned, we could leave the country at the first opportunity.

Thus, the seeds of our escape were planted. However, by this time the Berlin wall had been erected. The Iron Curtain between east and west made our prospects for escape much dimmer. Now it would be even more difficult to find our way to freedom.

Chapter Twelve

ESCAPE PLAN

1960-1965:
It Started When Veronika Was Three

The times were difficult for everyone. People were compelled to attend political meetings and rallies, march in the Labor Day parades on May 1st, and vote for the single party slate at elections. Although Jarda and I cared for one another, we found no joy living in a socialist state. We had our love for each other and our precious daughter Veronika, but had no freedom of expression, few personal choices, and little opportunity for individualism.

I'd given up my dream of becoming a physician in order to help Jarda get into college, and he had to give up his dream of an advanced degree in chemistry because of the persecution of the Communist regime. Neither of us had fulfilled our career dreams, and we were sure the dossier on Jarda in the party files was not favorable.

Even if Jarda was never prosecuted for being disloyal, we still lived under the control of the Party bosses. Our passports were held by the police, released only when a trip was approved by the Party. Permission was given or withheld according to the Party's views on the applicant's behavior, and the return trip had to be guaranteed. We knew we were unlikely to get such approval.

Since children gained access to a quality education based on the contents of their parents' dossiers rather than their own merit, we knew Veronika would not be allowed to go to college. That more than anything else gave us great emotional pain.

Veronika was a lively little girl who spent time with her friends Jirka, Peter, and a gypsy girl named Olinka. They played ball and other games just below our windows, and climbed trees at the end of our dead-end street. We lived in an apartment house that was said to have an unexploded bomb from the war buried in sand under the foundation. Living atop a loaded bomb struck me as symbolic of the times.

Our minds were preoccupied with the idea of escape. How would we do it? What would be the safest way? The first thing we thought of was to sew a giant balloon, take it to the hills in southern Moravia, fill it with helium, and ride the prevailing winds into Austria. This was technically feasible, but not at all practical. Being stopped with a balloon and helium tanks near the border would mean sure imprisonment.

It seemed more reasonable to go on a vacation somewhere near the border with the west and somehow get across. We found an East German travel agency offering vacations in Stralsund, Germany, on the northern coast. The vacation included an excursion boat ride in the Baltic Sea to view a famous Danish lightvessel positioned near the southmost coast of Denmark. We thought it possible to slip off the excursion boat into the water and swim to the Danish lightboat and freedom. The idea wasn't as crazy as it seemed. We learned that one Czech family succeeded in implementing it, their children and grandmother included. Afterward, the excursion boat was no longer permitted to sail that far.

Our first opportunity for foreign travel came in 1960. That summer, Jarda went on business trips to the Soviet-controlled states of Hungary and Russia. I was allowed to attend a scientific meeting in England. This was the first time I had visited the West, and for some reason my request to travel there was not met with any resistance from the Party. Maybe because they knew my family would remain behind in Czechoslovakia, or maybe I just slipped through the cracks.

England overwhelmed me. The places I visited were beautiful, but what impressed me most was how much it differed from the propaganda in the Czech Communist press, radio, and TV. After eight days in Cambridge and London, I returned home with the anguished soul of a schizophrenic. I felt like a homing pigeon compelled by some unknown force to return to my cage. At the same time, I wanted to fly free. I wanted so much for my family to be able to live like the people in England.

A year later, we applied to go for a vacation at a Black Sea resort in Bulgaria. Our objective was not to escape, but to establish the precedent of vacationing away from Prague. It would be good to spend time relaxing in the sun at the beach, where Veronika, who had just undergone inner ear surgery, could recuperate. As a rule, it was relatively easy to obtain permission to travel to other Communist countries.

However, one day before our scheduled departure, I received a telegram from the travel agency informing me the trip had been cancelled. It was common knowledge that such decisions originated with the secret police. I was worried they might have been closing in on Jarda.

In order to learn the reason for the cancellation, I went to the travel agency for an explanation. They claimed ignorance and equivocated. I tried to explain that we needed the vacation, not only because my young daughter was so looking forward to it, but also for her health. Eventually they referred me to a Ms. K— at police headquarters.

I waited a long time at police headquarters to see this woman. Finally, I was told Ms. K— would see me. A strict, no nonsense, middle-aged woman. she had my file in front of her. She asked me to tell her about my trip to England the previous year. She wanted to know why I had separated from the rest of the delegation the day after our arrival in England.

I told her the truth. I said the policewoman in charge of the travel group was only interested in shopping. My interest was to attend professional meetings and, in my free time, to visit as many museums, art galleries, and historical places as possible. Also, our daily allowance for both Cambridge and London was only five pounds. Instead of traveling with the group on public transportation, I walked from place to place to save money. My only crimes were not going shopping with the police guard and saving money on transportation.

She made me list everyone I met or talked with in England, and asked me to list everywhere I went. When I finished doing that, Ms. K— sent me home. She promised to inform me of the outcome of my request to vacation in Bulgaria.

Six hours before our scheduled departure, I received another telegram granting me permission to leave for Bulgaria with my family.

We spent two weeks on the sunny coast of socialist Bulgaria, and returned home when it was over. A simple vacation.

Yet, there is an interesting sequel to this story, proving that fate often plays tricks on people. About a year after, I boarded a streetcar for Vysocany, the 9th district in downtown Prague.

Sitting near me was a woman who was visibly upset. Her head was down and she was crying. We both got off the streetcar at the same stop. While alighting from the car, the woman lost her balance and I reached out to catch her. I asked her if there was anything I could do to help.

When she lifted her face, I recognized her. The secret police-woman, Ms. K—.

I asked if she remembered me and she said yes. She was barely able to walk so I helped her to the door of her apartment. She invited me in. She made tea and we sat at a table to talk. She was anxious to explain to me the reasons for her grief. Her health was failing so she no longer worked for the secret police. The tears were because her husband had abandoned her for a younger woman.

After a while, we touched on the events preceding my Bulgarian vacation. She told me my trip to England was what had prompted the cancellation. She had been at the travel bureau when I asked the agent for an explanation. She'd signaled him to send me to her at the police station. She told me that in England I was followed by a Czech agent. They were testing me to see if I would tell the truth. If I had left anything out, I would have been denied any more travel. Because she was able to verify my story, she approved our trip.

For the next several years, we took regular vacations away from Prague. It wasn't until 1965, however, that we undertook in earnest a plan to escape.

We had begun to hear rumblings that my resignation as the neighborhood representative along with our not joining the Communist Party meant we were disloyal. Our worry was that any increased attention might bring to light Jarda's record. If that happened, he stood a good chance of being arrested and prose-cuted. Not only could they make up an offense, but they might also resurrect his involvement with Mr. V— in Liberec or his anti-Communist rhetoric in his home town. This would mean we would lose him. Neither Veronika nor I would ever recover from such a loss.

We had to do something.

We decided to use our next vacation to escape. This time we would go to the Yugoslav coast and somehow get across the border to Italy. I've already told you that story. We tried and we tried and we tried. But we failed. It was the late summer of 1965 when we returned to Prague—out of energy and out of ideas.

We lived the next few months in fear and regret. There seemed to be no escape for us. Permission to travel anywhere outside of Soviet influence was impossible. Yet, Jarda's life might be in danger if we didn't leave.

Sometimes when hope has gone, opportunity presents itself.

An acquaintance of ours worked in the state-run travel agency Čedok. This agency had a monopoly on arranging foreign travel. This acquaintance told us she might be able to secure two seats for us on a three-day bus tour to Vienna to celebrate the New Year. The tour was for adults only. Children were excluded.

Getting a seat on such a tour was like winning a lottery. Seats were usually sold out before the tour was publicly announced. Austria was not under Soviet influence, so we had to obtain permission for the trip from the Communist Party in our work-place. Since they knew we would not be able to take Veronika with us, thus guaranteeing our return, permission was granted.

Jarda and I would be in Vienna on December 31st. Once we were there, we might be able to slip away from our Czech police guard. It was New Year's Eve after all, and there would be drinking and chaos in the streets. In all the confusion, we could find a way to sneak off. All we would have to do is hide Veronika away from the authorities in Prague—somewhere she would be happy and well cared for—until we found a way to get her out.

Jarda's mother and sister Hana lived in the small rural town of Týniště about 75 miles southwest of Prague, not far from the southern German and Austrian borders. There, Veronika would be well taken care of until we found the best way for her to join us.

Once we were in the West, we would be able to gather resources that we couldn't in Socialist Czechoslovakia. If Veronika was safely hidden away from the Prague authorities, we would have more time to seek out options. A good possibility was to save up our money and bribe an official. There was plenty of opportunity for that. We thought maybe we could obtain false papers for her in the West and she could come by train or plane. High quality false papers were not unheard of in those days.

Another approach would be to accomplish it legally. Perhaps we could get a foreign government or the Red Cross to intervene on humanitarian grounds. If all else failed, Jarda said he would re-enter Czechoslovakia under a different identity and smuggle her out. With his Alpine skiing experience and without me along to limit his options, he was sure he could do this.

We would have to talk to Veronika. She was now 8 years old.

We put our plan in place.

Chapter Thirteen

ESCAPE

1965-1966

Step 1: Making Veronika Safe

Christmas Day 1965 would be our 13th wedding anniversary. We would go to Týniště to celebrate, leave Veronika with her grandmother, and return to Prague in time for our tour to Vienna. Once in Vienna, we would make our escape. When the authorities investigated, they would find nothing but an empty flat in Prague. Hopefully, they would assume we got Veronika out by other means. Before they figured otherwise, we would find a way to really get her out.

After lunch one day, we took Veronika, then 8 years old, aside. We asked her, "Do you remember Opa and Hilda?"

Opa Leitner, my father's best friend, was a half-Jewish, half-German Czech lawyer. His wife Hilda was his German Czech wife. They were almost 60 years old when they left Czechoslovakia. Veronika had never known my father, but when she was younger Opa and Hilda had treated her like she was their own granddaughter.

"I remember them," she said.

I told her, "Well, Dad and I would like to leave the country like they did in order to find a better home for all of us. We don't know how long it will take us to find just the right place before we can send for you. Do you think you could stay with Grandma Caslavsky in Týniště while we look?"

She said yes right away, but I wanted to be sure she understood exactly what we were asking her to do. "We will visit Grandma for Christmas. If it's okay with you, you will stay there while we leave for a while. You would go to school in Týniště, and Aunt Hana would help to look after you. But I don't know how long we'll be apart. It could be as long as a few months."

I worried that if it took much longer than this, the authorities would figure out the whole plan and conclude that Veronika might still be in the country somewhere. Then if they found her, they could hold her hostage until we returned.

I told her, "We won't go unless you are sure you'll be content and happy while we're gone."

Veronika was a very intelligent little girl. I had confidence she understood what we were asking. I thought back to the abortion decision my mother left to me at 13. This wasn't that kind of decision, but we wouldn't go forward with the plan unless she was okay with it. If she didn't agree, we would have to face the very real possibility that Jarda would be arrested.

Years later, I saw the movie called *Sophie's Choice*. A Nazi officer forced a mother to choose which of her two children she would keep with her and which she would turn over to him. She pleaded with the officer, telling him she could never make such a choice, but he threatened to take both of them if she didn't choose one over the other.

When I saw the movie, I recalled the awful feelings I had in the winter of 1965. I could stay and face the possibility of losing my husband, or go and face the possibility of never seeing my daughter again. Like Sophie in the movie, I could never make such a choice.

Veronika could agree with our plan or not. Then I would leave the outcome to fate.

"Please, think this over and let us know how you feel about it before we leave for Grandma's at Christmastime. But you must say nothing to Grandma or anyone else because what we plan to do is not permitted."

My daughter nodded. She understood.

That same evening, Veronika sought us out. "I like it there, I can live happily with Grandma, you do not need to worry about me. But when you send for me, do you think you could already have a house, a puppy, and a baby? Please?"

ONE MONTH PRIOR TO OUR DEPARTURE, I LEARNED THAT I was pregnant. I was conflicted. If the three of us were already free, I would have welcomed another child into our family. But what if our escape required the kind of physical exertion that might cause a miscarriage? What if we were caught? I wouldn't want my child born in a prison or a work camp. What if we escaped, but I never saw Veronika again? Somehow when I pictured a child, I could only picture Veronika.

Three days before Christmas, Jarda and Veronika left to visit Grandma Caslavsky by bus. I entered a hospital near Prague, where a gynecologist acquaintance performed an abortion. I recuperated at home for two days, fighting the inner urge to tumble into the kind of depression I witnessed in my mother.

On Christmas Eve, I traveled by train to Týniště. I was

exhausted and depressed. The train was unheated. Was I doing the right thing? I didn't know. But some unknown force was compelling me forward.

Huddled in a seat alone with my arms grasping my knees and my feet atop the suitcase in front of me, I thought back to Christmases past—the precious times gathered together with my parents and grandparents, Grandpa Novak playing the violin, us singing Christmas carols and opening presents. Then there was the Christmas break that I met Jarda at Aunt Eva's. It was on another Christmas that we were married.

As I thought of all those Christmases, the English carol "Good King Wenceslas" kept going through my mind. The patron saint of our nation, King Wenceslas was the 10th century ruler of Bohemia. Many times, I had walked by his statue in the main square by the National Museum in Prague.

Here I was on Christmas heading toward an unknown fate. I felt good King Wenceslas holding me, my grandparents, my father, all of them holding me, holding my husband and child, perhaps my unborn child. It was as if they—not the train—were propelling me forward. My only solace, my only hope, came from these angels gathered around me and the auspiciousness of Christmas.

The trip took five hours. I arrived icy cold, as if my whole body were anesthetized. Jarda met me at the station.

We joined the rest of the family on their Christmas Day celebration without disclosing our secret to anyone. The next day, we went to visit Jarda's sister Hana who lived nearby. We told her about our plans and asked for her help with Veronika.

She said she would enroll Veronika in the local school by saying her niece's parents were both assigned to work in Prague and preferred their daughter be raised in the country. Living with her grandmother would likely raise no suspicion.

Hana also promised to help take care of Veronika. She asked us not to say anything to Grandma, as she thought it would be too upsetting for her to know what we were planning to do. Hana said she would find a way to tell her after we were gone.

Grandma gladly agreed to keep Veronika for the remainder of the Christmas break while Jarda and I went back to Prague and on to Vienna. She and Veronika accompanied us to the train station. When the train entered the station, Veronika began to cry. Jarda and I started to cry too.

Grandma was startled. "Why are you all crying?"

We gave no answer.

She thought for a moment. Then the blood drained from her face. "For God's sake, children! You're not coming back, are you?"

WHEN WE GOT BACK TO PRAGUE ON DECEMBER 27TH, I took Veronika's favorite things from the apartment—a doll carriage with her dolls, some clothes, underwear, and school books—and packed the them in a box. I went to the nearest railroad station and dispatched everything to Hana's address in Týniště.

Shortly after dark, I made another pass through the apartment, throwing our possessions with the most sentimental value into a small bag, which I then left on the doorsteps of a woman I trusted. I put a note inside asking her to save the few items for us.

On my way home, I rang the doorbell of our dear friend Franta. I wasn't sure whether I was going to tell him or not, but I at least wanted to see him one last time. Later he would realize it was our goodbye.

He stuck his head out of his apartment window and yelled,

"Hi Vera. Look, we have some people visiting, could you come by tomorrow?"

"Sure," I replied.

I called my mother and told her Jarda and I were going to Austria for New Year's Eve. I knew she had a dear friend there. When she was in high school, she had spent one summer in the Sudetenland border region between Czechoslovakia and Germany where a large minority of Germans lived before and during the second world war. She befriended an Austrian girl who was there visiting her aunt. The girls continued the relationship into adulthood, although without personal contact.

My mother gave me the woman's name and phone number so I could call and say hello. I didn't tell my mother what we were planning.

Step 2. The Trip to Vienna

THE TOUR BUS LEFT PRAGUE AT 11 PM ON DECEMBER 28th, a cold, raw, unfriendly night. We lined up and slowly filed onto the bus as a secret policeman in civvies examined and confiscated our passports. He introduced himself as the tour manager, but we all knew he was with the police. He had stood inside the bus at the head of the stairs while the rest of us waited outside in the rain.

The bus was not heated. Our tour manager sat in the front row behind the driver. When all of the passengers were present, our tour manager reached in his briefcase, which sat on the seat of the first row behind the driver, and pulled out a stack of sealed envelopes. He walked up and down the aisle of the bus, giving each of us a hard stare while handing us a sealed envelope.

He said, "As you were told, you are not to have with you more clothes and toiletries than is needed for a three-day stay in Vienna. You can carry no money or precious jewels. No documents. You will be thoroughly checked before crossing the border. All of this is spelled out inside these envelopes. In there you will also find your allowance of Austrian currency."

I don't remember how much money they gave us, but when Jarda saw it, he gave me a quick glance that I interpreted as, *These people are crazy. They have no idea what they're doing. This isn't enough money to feed a goldfish.* I knew he couldn't wait to be done with them.

I just stroked his arm and hoped he would keep it to himself.

The rain turned to snow. We had a number of precious gold coins with us, but I had no idea where Jarda had hidden them. Before we left, he told me, "Don't worry about it. It's best if you don't know."

I didn't carry any jewelry in my suitcase, but I wore my mother's gold necklace around my neck, tucked modestly under my blouse. Our motorcycle driver's licenses were stashed surreptitiously among dozens of scribbled papers with recipes on them that we'd inserted between the pages of a cookbook. I hoped they would figure the cookbook was my recreational reading and I was just a messy homemaker. The cookbook was packed in my suitcase next to a jar of Christmas cookies to distract their attention.

Our tour guide walked to the front of the bus and took his seat next to his briefcase. The snow turned back to rain, and we took off on the journey of our lives.

At about 4 o' clock in the morning, we entered the 10-kilometer-wide strip of the border region that was the no-man's land between Czechoslovakia and Austria. At the time, the region could only be entered with a special permit. Past the barbed wire fence, we saw a strip of terrain that had been laid bare. Jarda said it was to accommodate the minefields. Past the next barbed wire fence was an open area with guard towers similar to those in concentration camps. The area stretched in both directions parallel to the border. In between the guard towers were armed border patrol soldiers with dogs. They stood under makeshift canopies in the cold, wet weather.

A little way past the guard towers, the bus stopped before a group of army barracks. Our tour guide went inside. After a while he returned and announced that three passengers from the 40 or so people on the bus would be selected for a thorough luggage and body check. Jarda and I and another man were selected.

My heart pounded fast and hard in my chest, but I tried to act nonchalant, smiling at my fellow passengers as if I had just won a door prize.

A uniformed policeman ordered us off the bus and into the barracks. He told us to bring all of our luggage, emphasizing the word *all*. We were told to be ready for a body search too.

Jarda and the other man were taken away while I remained in the hallway with the policeman and one of the soldiers. I tried to watch out of the corner of my eye where they were taking Jarda and how they were treating him, but they quickly turned a corner and were out of view.

The policeman pointed to a wooden bench and told me to sit. I cheerfully obliged. "They are looking for a woman to search you," he said.

Time passed. I used the interlude to find just the right words to explain the cookbook in my suitcase. This reminded me of the jar of Christmas cookies. I asked the policeman if he would like a Christmas cookie while we waited.

Without hesitation he said, "Yes, that would be nice."

I unlatched the suitcase, took out the jar, and opened it for him. He took a cookie and thanked me profusely. I offered one to the soldier as well. He looked at the policeman and got a nod before he took one. During the time we waited, the policeman took two more without asking. I wondered if maybe I could get him to eat the cookbook.

Finally, the door opened in the back of the hallway and Jarda and the other passenger emerged, followed by another policeman. They were both red-faced. The police never found a woman to search me and they deemed my open suitcase harmless, so they let us all return to the bus.

We entered the bus in silence and it took off. Shortly thereafter, we entered Austria. Only then did I find the courage to ask Jarda what I was dying to know.

I grabbed his arm, cuddled up close, and whispered, "Did they find anything?"

He responded, "Of course not. Dumb bastards!"

In time I learned the search was thorough, but not thorough enough. They opened his camera but found nothing incriminating inside. The exposure meter at the time was carried separate from the camera. The searchers did not notice that the needle of the meter didn't move in the light. The mechanism had been removed, for it was here that Jarda had hidden the gold coins.

In retrospect, it had been foolhardy to smuggle the gold coins. Their discovery could have resulted in our being arrested and imprisoned. It's hard to explain, but the dolls I sent Veronika, the sack of keepsakes I left with my friend, and the gold coins all seemed so important at the time. Maybe the concept of freedom was just too big to comprehend, and these material things were what we could internalize.

Step 3. Setting Up our Getaway

EARLY THAT MORNING, WE ARRIVED IN VIENNA. AT THE hotel, our tour guide/secret policeman/gumshoe gave out the keys to our rooms, making sure he knew exactly which room each of us occupied. He could easily monitor us because there was only one stairway leading to the rooms. He gave us instructions for where and when we were to assemble for breakfast. He would stick with us at all times.

When we entered the dining room for breakfast, our secret policeman was seated at one of the tables with a clear view to the hotel stairway. Our plan was to somehow fade into the darkness. According to an old proverb, the darkest place is under the candle's flame. Jarda and I exchanged glances and headed for his table.

"May we join you?" we asked.

"Of course," he replied, smiling a bit and apparently pleased.

He engaged us in a generally sophisticated conversation—about nothing. Yet, we did get some information about the tour itinerary and were able to adapt our own plans accordingly.

The morning visit was to the Schonbrunn Castle. Since there were no Czech-speaking guides there, we would be allowed to explore by ourselves. We feigned interest in anything that lay in a direction away from our gumshoe. While he was out of sight, Jarda and I headed for the toilets, where we found telephones.

I dialed the telephone number given to me by my mother. The telephone rang several times before a female voice answered. "Anneliese, may I help you?"

When I introduced myself as Vera Kudrnka's daughter, Anneliese said she was delighted to hear from me. Jarda looked around and told me the coast was clear. In not very good German, I explained our situation. I told her we wanted to seek political asylum but still had a daughter in Czechoslovakia and were reluctant to take that step.

She said she might be able to help us. Her husband worked as an inspector at police headquarters. He would have access to information that could help us determine whether it was possible to do what we hoped to do. I told her that if it wasn't, we would return to Czechoslovakia. She asked us to call her back early the next morning.

Jarda and I returned to the rooms of the castle, keeping an eye out for our watchdog. When we spotted him, we wandered in his direction and spent the rest of the day in his company.

Step 4. No Turning Back

EARLY THE NEXT MORNING, I CALLED ANNELIESE AGAIN. This time it was her husband Rudi who answered. He had a pleasant baritone voice and a commanding demeanor. The first thing he told me was he was optimistic about getting Veronika out of the country. He mentioned the existence of precedents, which he would explain when we met. I told him I wasn't sure we would be able to meet because of our police keeper.

Then he asked point blank, "So what do you think, can I come and whisk you out of your hotel right now?"

I was shocked. I told Jarda, "He says we can get Veronika out. He wants to come and get us right now."

Jarda said, "Breakfast isn't for two hours yet. There's probably no one downstairs. We could go down and out the back door."

I told Rudi and he said, "I'll be outside waiting in 30 minutes."

Jarda and I gathered up what we could in our day packs and went downstairs for coffee. The day clerk was just coming on duty and was preoccupied with catching up on hotel matters with the night clerk. We dropped our packs in the corridor leading to the back door and went in the dining room for coffee.

When the 30 minutes were up, the night clerk had left and the day clerk came into the dining area to get his breakfast. We casually left the dining room and slipped out the back door with no one the wiser.

Rudi was there with the motor running. We jumped in his car and he drove away.

As we pulled out of the street behind the hotel, I held my breath, worried that somehow, some way, we would be caught. As he drove around corners and sped down long streets, I kept looking back. After all those years of Nazi occupation and Communist oppression, I was surprised no one was following us. It was so hard to believe we were free.

I tried to calm myself, but my mind was chattering furiously. We were driving to an unknown location and an unknown future. We may never set foot on Czech soil again. I thought of my grandfather Kudrnka helping me with my homework, of my grandfather Novak telling me ghost stories. And my own father. I worried about my mother's emotional well-being—how would she fare without me there? What if we get caught? Fear welled up inside me, and I looked to Jarda for relief.

All this time, he had remained quiet, looking out the car window. He had the expression of a man focused on the task at hand. He saw the look on my face, turned to me, and took my hand. I thought I detected tears building in his eyes.

"Vera, we are—" He hesitated in order to gain his composure. "We are free!"

A shot of adrenaline rushed through my bloodstream and into my heart, my body pulsing to its beat. My face got hot. Just as quickly, the sensations hardened and dropped like a giant rockslide into my gut. All I could think about was Veronika. We'd left Veronika behind!

Chapter Thirteen

LOSING OUR DAUGHTER

New Year 1966:
The First Week Without our Daughter

Rudi told us we were not out of the woods yet. The garret in his house on Weinrother Gasse in the 13th district of Vienna was rented to people employed in the Czechoslovak embassy. He cautioned us to converse only in German until he could make arrangements for us.

Speaking another language in a strange place made me feel like we had been transported to an alien world. But Rudy and Anneliese did everything they could to make us feel at home. Rudi was a swell chap possessed of a disarming Viennese charm and the capacity to understand others. Anneliese was the typical down-to-earth, pragmatic housewife. Their only son, Peter, studied law at the state university. They all treated us like close relatives visiting for the holidays.

Right after New Year's, Anneliese found us a small flat in the neighborhood by making a few calls to her friends. The rent was miniscule, but we still needed to find the money to pay it. We would also need income to pay for food, transportation, and other living expenses. The catch was that to make money we needed jobs, and to get jobs we needed papers, but to get papers we needed money.

We could have moved to a refugee camp on the outskirts of the city, but we preferred to be independent from the start. Here again, Anneliese proved helpful. She told me, "I know of an opportunity for you to work without papers doing housework and child care. I know you have a PhD and are capable of much more, but would you mind doing this kind of work?"

I replied immediately, "No, I would not mind—I would be thankful."

"The job is with a Mrs. Juranek. She already has a maid but needs additional help. If it is all right with you, she said you could start the job tomorrow."

The following day at 6 AM, I started working for Mrs. Juranek. The sooner we earned some money, the sooner we would get Veronika out.

An attractive woman, Mrs. Juranek was just and forthright. Her native language was German, but she could speak some broken Czech. Her husband owned several supermarkets and was unable to spend much time at home. They had five children— two sets of twin boys, and an older girl from her first marriage. Two of the boys were preschoolers and two were babies. The daughter was in her difficult teenage years. Whenever I looked at her, I wondered what Veronika would be like as a teenager. I wondered if we would be with her then.

Mrs. Juranek did the cooking, the maid tended to the children, and I did the cleaning. There was enough work for all of us. Around 10 AM, Mrs. Juranek liked to take a break. She would light a cigarette and say in her funny broken Czech: "Frau Doctor, would you like to have a coffee with me?"

We chatted about all manner of things. One time, she casually mentioned she had been a spy in her younger days, but did not mention for whom, and I did not ask. I recently learned that she died of Alzheimer's disease. I will always think of that kind and gentle woman as an angel who helped us when we needed it most.

One Month Without Our Daughter

JARDA FOUND A FULL-TIME JOB WITH A MANUFACTURER OF industrial instruments. I'm not sure how he was able to work without the proper papers. Maybe it was because he was from Socialist Czechoslovakia and the plant was owned by Russians.

Jarda's job wasn't very rewarding, but it provided enough money for us to get established in Vienna and obtain the proper papers to work legally. And as a result, I was able to go to work for the same company. After that, we were earning enough money to focus on getting Veronika out.

Rudi applied himself in an effort to get Veronika released, seeking connections with highly placed politicians who might intervene on our behalf. He succeeded in arranging an interview for me with the wife of the Minister of Finance. I did not know what to expect, but I was not prepared for the icy, almost hostile reception I received. I left with tears in my eyes and spent hours crying on a park bench near her mansion.

I later learned that she did drop a word on my behalf with a highly placed official, and this person sent a letter to the Czechoslovak government asking permission for an unnamed

Czech girl living with her grandmother to join her parents in Austria. The reply was as bad as it could be: *The parents abandoned the child. The parents can return. The child will stay here.*

As far as the Austrian government was concerned, this was their final response. I didn't know how, when, or if I would ever see my daughter again. I was again in the same position as my mother. She didn't know if she would ever see me again.

I cried on Jarda's shoulder. We did not know what to do next. We had managed to escape, but without our daughter joining us there would be no joy in our lives. Jarda tried to reassure me by saying we wouldn't give up. We would try other things. In the meantime, we should work hard and save as much money as possible. The more money we earned, the more options we would have.

Two Months Without Our Daughter

JARDA APPLIED HIMSELF TO HIS WORK WITH THE SAME dedication and intellect he used for everything he did. His job was to calculate the flow rates of various oils in the plant using a set of measurements. In the pre-computer age, the process took months. Jarda devised a new set of formulas that could cut that time to days, and he presented them to his supervisor, hoping for praise and maybe a promotion. His supervisor said it would take time to verify Jarda's method. In the meantime, he was quite cordial. He encouraged Jarda to read relevant literature and regularly invited him to his office for snacks of ham, horseradish, and croissants. They had long discussions on job-related applications. In the end, Jarda's shorter methods were not implemented because they proved too embarrassing to his supervisor, who had been using the other method for many years.

The irony was that neither calculation method yielded correct results because they required knowing the density of the oils. Because those densities were considered "state secrets" by the Russians, the wrong values were supplied to the calculators.

Socialism corrupted science as well as politics.

I wrote a letter about Veronika to the headquarters of the International Red Cross and to their president, Grace Kelly, the famous movie star and wife of Prince Rainier of Monaco. I explained our situation and asked for support. When I got no reply, I wrote several more times. My letters were never answered.

I also contacted the Human Rights Commission of the United Nations. They submitted a request to the Czechoslovak government for Veronika's release. After receiving a reply similar to the one sent to the Austrian government, the Commission also let the matter drop. As far as they were concerned, the case was closed.

As far as I was concerned, it was not.

At the time, a man named Honza worked at Vienna office of the American Fund for Czechoslovak Refugees Inc. He told us that due to both geography and politics, Austria was not able to be assertive in relationships with the Czech government. He advised us to move to America, where we could expect more powerful help in our quest to get our daughter back.

When we applied for an immigration visa from the American Embassy, we were told the waiting period was six to twelve months. The thought of leaving Austria was not a pleasant one. Austria reminded us of prewar Czechoslovakia with its prosperity, elegance, and deep historical roots. We knew next to nothing about America and did not know anyone who lived there. But we were desperate to try anything to get Veronika back.

I continued to work for the same manufacturing firm as Jarda. My supervisor was a small man with an exaggerated sense of self-importance and a bossy manner. There was not much to occupy us in that lab. Instead of allowing me to spend my time in some useful activity, he had me repeatedly polish the laboratory glass. When a problem popped up, he gave it to me to solve and then took credit for it himself. But I didn't care. I spent all my energy on our efforts to get Veronika out of Czechoslovakia.

Four Months Without Our Daughter

A COLONEL FRANTIŠEK MORAVEC, THE FORMER HEAD OF pre-Communist Czechoslovak Military Intelligence during the war, heard about our plight. He invited us to visit him. When we did, Moravec asked to hear our life stories, the truth and nothing but the truth. He listened, then said he would see what he could do.

My boss's boss sent me to an adjacent plating plant to solve a recurring problem of uneven thickness in the galvanization process. After I spent a few days on the shop floor, I figured out the coating issue was due to the uneven densities of the electric currents. I discovered that, for the most part, this resulted from workers' mistakes when hanging the parts in the plating vats.

I reported my findings to my boss's boss. This accomplishment resulted in an offer to double my salary in return for taking on more responsibility. Although this was welcome news, I said thanks but no thanks. Why?

Our application for an immigration visa to America had been approved—in six weeks instead of the usual six months. I don't know if any of the people we contacted had a hand in expediting our application, but the result came unusually fast.

The reality of leaving Austria panicked us. Jarda was still entertaining the idea of sneaking into Czechoslovakia and smuggling Veronika out—a plan I firmly opposed. After leaving Czechoslovakia in order to save Jarda, I couldn't support his going back there. Being without my daughter and my husband would be more than I could survive.

We returned to the American embassy and told them we were reluctant to leave because we continued to hope that Veronika would be released to us in Austria. For that reason, we requested a delay in the issuance of the visa, which was granted by a sympathetic lady at the embassy.

Six Months Without our Daughter

As time went on and our hopes faded, we decided to accept the visa. June marked 6 months since we'd left Veronika with her grandmother. We had received word that she was happy in Týniště, but now the authorities knew about her. So, she was effectively being held hostage, and we faced the risk that she could be in danger. We knew we had to find a sure way of getting her out. America seemed like our best, if not our only chance to accomplish this.

Chapter Fourteen

AMERICA

June 1966:
Refugees

We booked two seats on a refugee plane that was scheduled to leave Vienna in early June. The fare was $100 each, prepaid for us by the American Fund for Czech Refugees, along with our binding promise to repay the amount within a year. We hoped the Fund for Refugees would help us to find work, although they could give no assurances.

We had saved about $400, which would have enabled us to survive for about four months in Austria. We also had another $200 that had been sent to us by an old school friend, my cousin's husband, Dr. Dolejsek, a one-year fellow at the National Research Council in Ottawa. We knew he had meager savings, and we appreciated his help so much.

We didn't know $600 was far short of what we would need for a start in America.

Before departing Vienna, we answered help wanted ads in various American scientific journals. For a short while, it seemed we would be in luck. Corning Glass Works in North Carolina was looking for research personnel, and its director corresponded with us. Before we left Austria, however, his final reply arrived with the bad news: we could not be employed at that installation because they worked on classified government projects and we lacked security clearances. Because we had come from a Communist-controlled country, we had faced a similar situation in Austria. In fact, the director of a plant in Linz asked us to prove we were not spies. How do you do that?

The American Fund for Czech Refugees had chartered an old twin engine propeller plane. We were instructed not to take any food with us as there would be food on the plane. The plane made a stopover in Frankfurt, where more refugees with children boarded, cramming it to capacity. Shortly after takeoff, it became clear there was not enough food on board for everyone.

In the wee hours of the morning, the plane made a refueling stop in Shannon, Ireland. We tried to get some food, but everything was closed and it was impossible to get even a cup of coffee. I remember standing at a fence at the airport, tired and hungry. I stared up at the stars, wondering what fate lay ahead of us.

We landed at Kennedy Airport in New York at about noon on a very hot summer day. A man from the American Fund for Czech Refugees was waiting for us at the gate. He divided us into two groups: those who had relatives or friends and a place to stay, and those who did not. Jarda and I were in the latter group.

The man gave us some general instructions, but he was busy with the arrival of so many refugees that it seemed his main concern was to get rid of us as soon as possible. He put us in a taxi, prepaid the fare, and sent us to what he described as a reasonably priced hotel in Manhattan.

Depressed and exhausted, we watched the unfamiliar scenery pass by the windows of the taxi. We drove past cemeteries and rows of uniform, modest houses, then crossed the river into Manhattan. The cab driver let us off on a dusty, grimy, tree-less street, in front of a hotel. We were in the northern section of Manhattan, known for its poverty and crime. We were in Harlem.

We entered the unappealing building and were given the key to our room. It was filthy and reeked of stale tobacco smoke and human odors. The hotel seemed more like a brothel than a rest haven for tourists.

We turned right around and went back to the front desk. Jarda demanded our money back. The clerk didn't seem to care one way or the other. Out on the sidewalk with our suitcases, we felt abandoned and desperate. Now what?

Another refugee family arrived in a cab and we told them not to bother checking in. We must have been quite a sight: four European refugees with suitcases in front of a bordello in Harlem. We were hot, hungry, and at a loss as to what to do next.

The men looked around a bit and returned with a grilled chicken from a street vendor. We dined in silence with our laps as our table and our suitcases as chairs. In Europe, we could have walked into a sidewalk café, a restaurant or pub and we would have been able to quench our thirst and easily get information about lodgings. In Harlem, we had to settle for a rundown place with a big, blinking BAR sign. We entered and ordered mugs of beer.

We made our inquiries of the locals in the bar. Half were

white, the other half black. None of them understood us. Most seemed suspicious of us because of our broken English, the rest were uninterested in our plight. Fortunately, an older black man joined our table and responded patiently to our questions, repeating his answers when he thought we did not understand. The man also drew a sketch for us with directions to the bus station.

It was obvious to us that with the little money we had, we would not be able to stay in New York very long. We needed to get out, but had no idea where to go.

Since our only contact had been with the director of the Corning Glass plant, that evening, we boarded an overnight bus for Raleigh, North Carolina.

The next morning, we arrived at the Raleigh bus station, which was situated in an old, run-down area on the edge of the downtown. This area was not acclaimed for its cleanliness or aesthetic appearance. Nevertheless, we were able to use the bus station washrooms to clean up and revive ourselves. We had coffee in a shop across the street, then placed a call to the director of the Corning research facility.

We did not wish to impose on Dr. Megla, but we were desperate. We did not know anyone else in the entire country! So, we hoped we could consult with him about how to find work. Based on our experiences so far in America, however, our expectations were low.

We got lucky. Dr. Megla immediately grasped our situation as he had been a refugee from East Germany. He sent a company limousine to pick us up and take us to a nice motel in a nice area on the periphery of the city. The chauffer told us our meals and lodging would be paid for by the company. The director would come for us on the following day.

Dr. Megla was very kind to us. He told us he would not be

able to locate jobs for us himself, but he'd asked his secretary to come in the next day, a Saturday, to help us write resumes in good English. She would mail them to agencies with whom he'd had contact. Realistically speaking, he said, we would not land a job in our field in less than three or four months. If a company was interested in our applications, they would invite us for an interview. Then we would need to travel to the interview. In short, landing a job would take time.

Dr. Megla gave us a tour of the Corning Research facilities, which were very impressive. We thanked him and left for downtown Raleigh again.

This time we found a room in the garret of an old hotel. The room was tiny but air-conditioned, which we welcomed. The heat outside was devastating, with a record draught forecast for the year.

Our main concern was making our scant savings last. We also talked about returning to Austria while we still had enough money to do so. The food didn't help our desire to leave. The American bread was mushy and tasteless with no crust. Butter was salty, and the beer tasted like cough medicine. Only later did we learn that "root beer" was a soda pop, not a pilsner.

Jarda met a German fellow in a nearby pub who offered to take him to his boss, a cement contractor. Apparently, there was a shortage of laborers.

"Do you know how to lay cement sidewalk?" he asked Jarda.

Jarda had no idea. "Sure," he replied, and they went to see the boss.

The boss agreed to hire Jarda. But then he asked for his social security number.

"What is a social security number?" Jarda replied.

The next day, we walked a hot eight miles to the Social Security Office. Somehow our refugee status qualified us for Social

Security numbers and the process took only about 15 minutes. Unlike in Czechoslovakia, we didn't have to ask for any special favors or bribe any government officials.

We didn't know if the cement job would last or even if Jarda's little lie would be found out and he would be fired. But as had occurred so many times in our journey, fate stepped in.

The phone rang around 10 PM. I thought it must be a wrong number, and I was surprised when the voice on the other end greeted me in German. I had learned enough German in school and in Austria to be able to converse freely.

"I am Erich Christian from Raleigh," the man said. "You don't know me, but I heard about you from Dr. Megla."

Dr. Megla had again been our guardian angel.

Mr. Christian continued, "My wife and I come from Austria. One of my grandparents was a Czech."

It's funny how that one Czech grandparent of a German man —a stranger on the telephone when you are thousands of miles away from home—can make you feel like kin.

He said, "My wife and I have three children. My wife is currently in a hospital for cancer surgery. I need somebody to help me take care of the house, to cook for my family, and to help my wife after she comes home. Would you be interested?"

I replied immediately, "Yes, of course I would."

He said Jarda and I could live in the guest room behind their house.

The next morning, we moved to the Christians' home.

They were a lovely family. Their faith matched their name — they were true Christians. They believed in God, and God was in their hearts. The children were independent, smart, candid, and like their parents, congenial.

Once Lotte Christian returned from surgery, I formed a close bond with her. I also had an affinity for her youngest, Elizabeth.

She was Veronika's age and had very similar manners. She reminded me so much of Veronika that I always felt a pang in my heart when she came running to me.

Professor Christian loved good cooking. He liked me to make Czech dishes. His favorite was *škubánky*, a simple country treat made from potatoes, sugar, flour, and lots of butter.

Professor Christian wrote to many of his friends with inquiries about jobs for us. Neighbors from across the street offered us the use of their house while they were on vacation in exchange for keeping it secure and feeding their pets. Such trust in complete strangers was a new experience for us. I have since learned that such hospitality is common both in America's South and Midwest.

Lotte was very weak when she first came home from the hospital, but she succeeded in uplifting my spirits with her assurances that Veronika would soon be able to join us. Lotte was one of the kindest people I have ever met, and I was so happy to see her gain back her strength. However, this made it clear I wouldn't be needed much longer.

One day Professor Christian came home with good news. His friend, Dr. Rustom Roy from the Materials Research Laboratory of the Pennsylvania State University, had written that he had an opening for both of us in his laboratory. The jobs would be temporary, but would give us the opportunity to prove ourselves in our own field. But if we wanted the jobs, we would have to start immediately.

The Christians encouraged us to accept the offer. The very next day, we boarded a bus and headed for Pennsylvania.

The Christians were our friends for life, and we kept in touch with them. We were deeply saddened five years later when Lotte succumbed to her illness. Eventually, Erich remarried and the children left to pursue their own lives. We maintained contact with Erich and his second wife. On occasion, we visited them and Eric was always his effervescent, energetic self, playing Mozart on his Steinway piano and enjoying good food, wine, and conversation. I shall always cherish his kindness to us as well as Lotte's memory.

Chapter Fifteen

PENN STATE

Fall 1966:
Nine Months Without our Daughter

We changed buses in Harrisburg, Pennsylvania. The bus station there was really dirty. I tried to clean up and make myself presentable. Maybe my nerves were shaken at the time because the filth and garbage in the rest room almost made me vomit. I wished we had never left South Carolina.

I was able to control myself enough to clean up and get back on the bus. We arrived at the college around noon. It was not what I expected. Penn State University had a large campus that spread over almost half the town. The town was named State College and the college portion was called University Park. There were many shops and cafes in the streets abutting the campus. And there were forests with lakes and beaver ponds on the periphery. The entire area was serene and beautiful. With some 50 thousand students, Penn State was prominent in agricultural sciences as well as other fields such as geochemistry and material science.

Because we arrived at the end of the summer semester, we had our pick of apartments for rent. We found a room with bunk beds at Mrs. Fletcher's on Allen Street. She was in her eighties, somewhat deaf but charming and good-natured. Once a week she drove her car to the supermarket, sailing through the streets unperturbed in the self-assured manner of a tank driver. Fortunately, the market was only a couple of blocks away and other traffic was not severely tested.

The Materials Research Laboratory was located at the far end of campus. To get there on foot took a half-hour. We walked this distance each morning and evening, enjoying the greenery of the park-like surroundings of the campus.

South Carolina had little rain. The first time I saw puffy, cumulus clouds in the Pennsylvania sky, I whispered to myself, "Oh, God, am I not glad there are also clouds in America!" My English in those days was still a little out of order. When I saw violets in the grass with the clouds overhead, it reminded me of home.

At the lab we came under the aegis of Dr. Roy's secretary, Helene, an older lady who was the soul of the enterprise. She gladly became a surrogate mother to us, as well as some 50 other graduate students and professors. We were delighted to find out Jarda was to work for Professor Vand, also a native of Czecho-slovakia. Dr. Vand had managed to escape shortly after the Communist takeover in 1948, first to England, and later to the United States. Unfortunately, when we met him he was already ill with cancer. He died shortly thereafter.

Jarda's new supervisor was Professor Vedam, an Indian scholar who specialized in optical and other properties of materi-als. I worked with Don Strickler, a graduate student who studied photoconductive glasses. He was a diligent student, just like the others in the lab.

I was not only a stranger to the US, but also one of just a few women among so many men in the lab. It was a lonely existence. Unless they needed something specific, they avoided talking to me. Their most frequent topic of discussion was football. I did not know a thing about American football and therefore could not join in.

When I learned that they were betting on the games in a weekly football pool, I asked Don for an explanation of scoring and team standings. I then studied the last few weeks' results and decided to join the pool. I didn't understand football, but I did understand statistics.

On Monday Don came to me smiling. "Vera, you won the pool!"

"No kidding," I responded in a proud tone.

I don't remember the amount I won, probably somewhere between $10 and $12. At the end of the week I bet again, and I won again. And again, a third time. From then on, I was considered one of the boys and included in all their conversations. That was my biggest win!

One weekend, Don invited me to join the group at a Penn State home game. The football team was called the Nittany Lions, which they explained was a mountain lion that roamed central Pennsylvania in the 1800's—although unconfirmed sightings frequently occurred after college drinking parties. During the game, my coworkers also explained each tactical move on the football field. When it got cold, I was offered a sip of whiskey hidden in a coke bottle.

Penn State won that day, and so did I. I had found a home in America.

From the start, Jarda and I tried to find allies to help us

secure Veronika's release. When I walked into town one day, I noticed a sign that said FBI. I was not at all sure the FBI was the place to start my search, but I had to start somewhere. So, I went inside.

In the office, a polite, older man named Mr. D— listened to our story. He told me the FBI was not in a position to help, but he referred me to the office of the university president. He said I would find someone there who was in charge of public relations and they might be able to help me.

I followed his advice, and was referred by the president's secretary to Mr. Cattell, a young man who worked high up in the university administration. He was a pleasant, tall man who heard me out politely. He said he had no idea how to help me, but when he went to Washington, D.C. again, he would make inquiries and report back to me. I thanked him and left with the feeling that the American people cared.

One day, Helene summoned Jarda and me to the office. Dr. Roy asked us about our wellbeing and our future job prospects. I told him how the previous week I had been offered a job in the lab of a mining research institute in Pittsburgh and we were waiting to find out if Jarda, who had an interview scheduled for the following week, would also be offered a job there.

Dr. Roy nodded, then made us a counteroffer. He proposed that we continue to work in the Materials Research Laboratory on a temporary basis at our present salaries, which was around $500 a month for each of us. Not only was that a fair wage, but also, we were learning a lot in the lab and had access to the latest instrumentation techniques. An additional ingredient sweetened the deal: Jarda could pursue the PhD degree he had been denied by the Communist Party in Czechoslovakia.

Jarda and I told Dr. Roy we would talk it over.

Our primary objective was still to find a way to get our

daughter. We discussed this with Professor and Mrs. Mares, long time Penn State residents of Czech origin. The couple had befriended us and they wanted us to stay. Even though we could earn more money in Pittsburg, we had a better chance of getting Veronika if we stayed put. We had found friends, and help, but in Pittsburg we would be starting over.

We accepted Dr. Roy's offer. Poor Jarda had no idea what he was getting into, what undertaking graduate studies at a school like Penn State meant. Yet, neither he nor I ever regretted our decision.

Registration for the PhD program was first on the agenda. For that, Jarda needed the approval of the dean. Helene arranged an interview.

"Which university did you attend, Mr. Caslavsky?" asked the dean.

"Charles University in Prague, sir," replied Jarda.

"You must excuse me, but I have to check the accreditation of this institution for the record."

The dean pulled a dusty book off the shelf. He seemed to be having trouble finding Charles University.

Jarda thought maybe his English hadn't been clear. He said, "That's spelled C-H-A—"

"I know how it's spelled. The European universities aren't listed alphabetically. They're listed by the year of their founding."

"In that case," Jarda suggested, "Charles University should be found on the first page, sir."

Indeed, it was, and the dean approved Jarda for graduate school.

Next was registration. There we faced the question of whether we would pay tuition as residents or non-residents. The Pennsylvania residency requirement was four years. We hadn't been there that long, but Jarda successfully argued he should be considered a resident, for he had no other home. This brought the cost of tuition to $4 per credit, while non-residents paid five times that amount.

As a married student, Jarda got a small inexpensive apartment in a building adjacent to our lab. We paid $60 a month rent, utilities included.

The biggest hurdle was the courses Jarda had signed up for. After his first day, he came home depressed.

"Was it hard?" I asked.

"I don't know," was his reply. "I didn't understand a word of what was said."

The course was taught by Dr. Roy's wife, who was Indian, and who had a manner of speaking rapidly in a very soft voice. The only way Jarda was able to keep up was that he requested of her — and she agreed to allow him — to read her scripts ahead of class, which he did until the end of the semester.

Between work and his studies, Jarda was busy seven days a week until midnight or later. I continued working in the lab. Occasionally I got to go to a concert or play bridge at the university club.

Then came the call from Mr. Cattell.

Chapter Sixteen

A GLIMMER OF HOPE

Winter 1966:
A Year Without our Daughter

I t was evening when Mr. Cattell called to say he had just returned from Washington, D.C., where he had discussed our situation with Senator Clark of Pennsylvania. The senator agreed to explore the possibilities for getting Veronika to the US. This was kind of him as we were not US citizens and thus not eligible to vote.

Later we learned that the senator invited the Czechoslovak ambassador to dinner, then asked him to intercede on behalf of the reunification of our family. This the ambassador was unwilling to do, and he pointed to an ongoing dispute about Czech and Slovak gold held by the US government. The gold was to compensate US citizens for properties confiscated by the Communist regime. The ambassador told the senator to return the gold, then they could talk again.

This was a setback, but I felt hopeful in that we at least had a direct route by which to get Veronika back—Mr. Cattell to Senator Clark to the Czech ambassador. We sent letters and money to Veronika and Grandma regularly, so we knew our daughter was happy in Týniště. All we had to do was wait for US-Czech relations to improve.

As Christmas neared, Jarda finished up his first semester exams. I thought back to the family holidays and was depressed about having this one without Veronika. Two friends, Hans from Germany and Jean from France, saw how down I was. They were postdoctoral fellows at the university and were going to Florida for the Christmas break. They insisted we join them. Nothing in government was going to change over the holidays.

We drove south along the enchanting coasts of the Carolinas and Georgia. We stopped in St. Augustine, Florida, where we saw an exact replica of Michelangelo's David amid the hibiscus flowers and the lush green palm trees. We continued down to the Everglades, then all the way south until we arrived at Ernest Hemingway's house in Key West.

There were a lot of firsts on that trip. First time we had time off since we'd left Czechoslovakia. First time we watched dolphins swimming in an aquarium. First time we saw alligators and flamingos in the wild. First time being in Florida. It wouldn't be our last.

Veronika was foremost on our minds when we returned to work at Penn State, and we were wondering what steps we might take next. One student in the lab, a black man, offered to go to Czechoslovakia to marry her and bring her out of the country as his wife. His well-meaning offer could not be accepted because Veronika was now only 10 years old.

Jarda thought about contacting the CIA to ask for a false passport with which he could reenter Czechoslovakia and fetch Veronika. We heard the idea had been tried by a Czech refugee in

Sweden. However, the Czech authorities had learned of the plot and they arrested the man at the border. Still, Jarda was willing to try.

My nerves could not have borne the stress if Jarda had embarked on something that risky. The probability of success for such a plan was extremely low. The Czech authorities were very suspicious, and the Czech Police kept a vast file of fingerprints.

I convinced Jarda to wait for news from Senator Clark.

⊗⧕⊗

June 1967: 18 Months Without our Daughter

SIX MORE MONTHS PASSED. OPA AND HILDA LEITNER visited us from Germany. Because Opa and my father had been friends since their student days, Opa became my surrogate father when my father died at age 40. Our relationship had been a close one ever since.

The Leitner's wanted to explore the US west on their vacation, and they asked us to join them. There was little change in US-Czech relations, so we decided to go. We all drove west in our Ford auto we'd named "Joe." Our trip had just started when troubles commenced and the car began to overheat.

Jarda stopped at a garage on his assumption the thermostat needed to be replaced. Instead, we left with a new battery which the mechanic insisted would correct the problem. A few miles later, the car began to overheat again.

A second mechanic was absolutely sure that the problem would be corrected by installing new ignition cables. Nevertheless, we made a third stop at yet another gas station, where Jarda finally succeeded in getting a new thermostat. Then our Joe ran for the rest of the trip without any problems.

In three days' time, we arrived in Denver. As we observed the countryside, we thought it most closely resembled Poland with all the corn and vast fields. Midway through Kansas, a road sign warned us the next gas station was 100 miles ahead. So, we turned off the highway to a small rural station in the middle of nowhere. The proprietor sprayed water on the car to cool it down as we stood nearby, stretching our legs and talking in Czech.

The gas station owner began to speak in fluent Czech. He was a native American, but his grandparents came from Bohemia. The man had lived all his life in Kansas and never visited Czechoslovakia. "Everyone around here speaks Czech," he said. "Including the fellow in the truck driving towards us now."

He explained now the nearby town of Wilson was known as the Czech capital of Kansas. We regretted that our tight schedule prevented us from visiting Wilson. We noted that it might be a place to visit in the future.

When we arrived in the Rockies, we had to rest the car more often in order to cope with the altitude. We had to cool it so it would help us negotiate the steep inclines. We explored the land, sometimes by instinct, sometimes using maps. We visited state parks, monuments, and reservations. We were impressed by the one thousand-year-old Indian dwellings of Mesa Verde, as well as by the desert cacti and the canyons of the Colorado River. We were as impressed by the smaller, more colorful gorges of Zion, Bryce, Walnut, and Cedar Breaks as we were by the Grand Canyon. America was a beautiful country.

One night we slept under the broad skies of the Painted Dessert, surrounded by petrified wood—scorpions and other poisonous creatures be damned. The Grand Tetons resembled the Slovak High Tatra mountains. The geysers, waterfalls, and various land formations of Yellowstone Park were true beauty on earth.

The Leitner's had a plane to catch in New York in less than a week. We had to cover at least 600 miles a day to make it back in time. Unfortunately, we were rear-ended by a sedan driven by some locals, and this put our Joe out of commission for good.

That night we stayed at the farm of Mrs. Winter, the mother of a Penn State colleague. She turned out to be an angel in disguise. Somehow, she prevailed on the insurance agent to pay us immediately for our car. We bought a large secondhand Chrysler Fury III. The car sailed like a ship, enabling us to make it to New York in time for the Leitner's flight.

Back at Penn State, we settled into waiting for a change in the status quo. Jarda was more agitated and emotional than I was. He seemed to be focused on the terrible things the Russians and their Czech Communist agents were capable of doing. I was more focused on keeping the situation calm and hopeful. Although we always told Veronika the truth about what was going on, I tried to do so in such a way that she would not become frightened.

We waited and waited. Then one day everything changed.

Chapter Seventeen

GETTING VERONIKA OUT

January 1968

Day 1 of Prague Spring

We had spent two years without our daughter when Alexander Dubček was elected First Secretary of the Communist Party of Czechoslovakia. Word spread that things in Czechoslovakia were going to change again. Dubček ran on a platform of "Socialism with a Human Face," and he proposed to loosen restrictions on media, speech, and most importantly, travel. Czechoslovakia was at Day 1 of what the world called the Prague Spring.

DAY 30

A month later, we heard from my Uncle Eda, now a physician in Prague. He told us several *apparatchiks* in the government had been replaced by decent people and he would file papers to obtain a permit for Veronika to emigrate.

Senator Clark called us of his own accord soon after that. He told us he was to have dinner with the Czech ambassador again and would raise the matter of Veronika's release once more.

Day 90

In April, we got word from Grandmother Caslavsky that the permit Uncle Eda had requested was granted. Uncle Eda told us there were details to be worked out by a lawyer. The permit required that Veronika revoke all rights to property or inheritance she might have in the country.

This was not a problem for us. Our daughter was worth more to us than anything of monetary value. It took several weeks to work out the legalities with the Czech authorities. After Veronika signed away her rights of inheritance, she was granted a permit to emigrate. She needed only to secure a Czech passport and a US visa.

Day 120

In May, Senator Clark's office sent a request to the US embassy in Prague to issue a visa as soon as Veronika presented her passport. Things were falling into place. We couldn't believe it.

We called Pan American Airways right away to find out if we could pre-pay for her flight. They understood the situation and offered to use their contacts in the Czech government to help expedite the paperwork. They looked into it, and by the end of May Pan Am informed us the Czech passport had not yet been issued.

. . .

Day 150

As the summer began, things got quiet. We understood how slowly the wheels of government sometimes turn, so we waited patiently. Maybe it would be more accurate to say we waited impatiently, but in a controlled manner. This served our purposes because we also had to consider the emotional impact on Veronika of leaving Czechoslovakia. She was happy there with her Grandmother and she had a school year to finish out.

We also had to consider Grandma's feelings. Jarda's mother was very attached to our daughter. She was getting old and was nervous about what to pack and what Veronika should leave behind. We corresponded with both of them, being careful to give them time to adjust. We recruited Aunt Hana and Uncle Eda to help with the transition.

Day 180

When July came and we still had no word about the passport, we started to grow worried. The Soviet Union did not like the reforms taking place in Czechoslovakia, and Dubček was under attack politically. The news deepened our concerns.

Day 188

On July 8th, the Monday morning after the long Fourth of July weekend, Jarda lost patience. He called Pan Am and asked for help in speeding up Veronika's departure. They said they would work it and get back to us.

. . .

Day 208

Three weeks later, when we still had not heard back from Pan Am, Jarda called again. They said they had handled it and were surprised we hadn't heard from the embassy. They promised to look into what went wrong.

Day 212

Four days later, Pan Am informed us the US embassy in Prague had sent us a message a couple of weeks earlier and had been waiting for our response. We never got any such message. Pan Am said the embassy needed a statement from us confirming that we were financially able to support Veronika. Somehow that simple request had been lost, wasting precious time.

We immediately contacted Mr. Cattell, who said he would help us draft the documents. Late that evening, a Sunday, we met in his office, where he helped us write the letter. He then directed us to the home of a notary public for signing and a seal.

The next day, we got the document notarized. Jarda got in the car and drove all night to deliver it to Senator Clark in Washington, D.C.

Day 216

Senator Clark immediately arranged for the transmission of the letter by diplomatic mail to the US Embassy in Prague. It was due to arrive on August 9th.

Day 218

On August 8th, I called Uncle Eda in Prague and asked him

to take Veronika to the US embassy the next day. The visa was issued on Friday, August 9th.

DAY 223

On Tuesday, August 13, 1968, two and a half years after we left her with her grandmother in Týniště, Veronika boarded a plane to America. She was three weeks shy of 11 years old and traveling alone aboard a Pan Am flight to New York.

We were waiting for her at the arrival gate at JFK Airport. The sun shone and the air was hot and still. My heart was pounding in my chest and I held tightly to Jarda's arm, fearful that somehow the plane wouldn't come or, when it did, she wouldn't be on it. I watched from behind a chain-link fence, my heartbeat loud in my ears.

I can't describe the joy I felt when a Pan Am jumbo jet taxied toward us. I held my breath as the ground crew wheeled a staircase over to the plane and opened up the exit door. The ground crew on the tarmac then opened the gate to the chain-link fence.

The best thing I could ever imagine was about to take place. But it seemed to take forever for anyone to come out the aircraft door. The anticipation was almost too much to bear. It was like my baby was being born all over again.

Finally, a stewardess emerged from the plane, one hand shielding her eyes from the bright sun. Her other hand held the hand of a little girl.

Veronika!

She walked down the stairs, and Jarda bolted through the open gate with me right behind. At the bottom of the stairs, we hugged one another. Veronika was once again in our arms. Eight days later, On August 21, 1968, Warsaw Pact troops invaded Czechoslovakia and again shut down the borders.

Chapter Eighteen

A CHILD IN AMERICA

1968/1969 School Year:
Veronika's 5th Grade in Pennsylvania

Once Veronika was safe with us, we thought our troubles would be over. What we didn't realize is that a new and unexpected set of problems would arise. This time our troubles were with our daughter.

Did Veronika like America? Yes and no, I think.

When Veronika got off the plane, she didn't have the same joy on her face Jarda and I had. She was detached, reticent. And why not? Everything she was experiencing was new and unfamiliar. She had left the little village of Týniště with a few thousand people in tile-roofed, stone and stucco houses. Now she was in New York City with millions of people in giant skyscrapers.

I knew her to be a very intelligent little girl, and thoughtful. I could see she was taking it all in. She had probably constructed images in her mind of what America would be like, and now she was correlating that with the reality—updating as she went along.

There was also a certain sadness about her. She had left Grandma Caslavsky behind, not knowing if she would ever see her again. Uncle Eda and Aunt Hana were thousands of miles away in Czechoslovakia. All her cousins and friends were there. She had come to an alien world.

We decided it would be best to take a few days off and show her some of the beauty of the country. We drove down the coast of North Carolina to Cape Hatteras. Two of our friends from the university had a daughter the same age as Veronika. With their permission, we brought Gina with us. This turned out to be a good move. The two girls got along well despite the language barrier.

In September when school started, Veronika was the right age for 6th grade, but because I was worried about her lack of skill in English, I decided to let her repeat 5th grade. She could concentrate on learning English without the burden of too much new material. This was a big mistake.

I had failed to consider the social implications of sending her to a class with younger children. To compound my error, Veronika's life experience, that is, growing up in the great city of Prague and then building a new life in rural Týniště, had matured her past her years. She probably would have been a better fit socially with kids in the 7th grade.

We had unwittingly burdened her with a problem that would follow her each year throughout her public schooling.

According to her teacher, an older woman with whom I frequently communicated, Veronika was often bored in class. If Jarda and I spoke English at home, Veronika would doggedly resist and respond in Czech—if she responded at all. The teacher advised us to let Veronika solve the language difficulty her own way, at her own pace—at least for the time being.

Instead of participating in class, Veronika wrote letters to her Czech friends. She sometimes sang Czech songs to herself. Some of the other children ridiculed the odd-looking hen-scratching's in her letters and the strange words coming out of her mouth. This drove Veronika deeper into her own world. When the teacher intervened, asking the children to put themselves in Veronika's place, little changed. Children can be very cruel.

After about a month, Veronika came home from school with a solemn look on her face. She announced that she thought she understood what had been taught in math class that day. This was real progress, and her teacher, Jarda, and I took great pleasure in her achievement.

As time went on, the teacher noticed Veronika was beginning to interact verbally with the other kids. When they asked her a question, she would respond. But when the teacher addressed her, Veronika would not answer. She wondered if Veronika might be afraid of her, or if perhaps there was some cultural norm the teacher didn't understand.

When we asked Veronika about this, she gave us a simple answer. "I understand the children but I don't understand the teacher."

The teacher laughed when I shared this with her. We agreed to give it more time.

From then on, we noted almost daily progress at school. Veronika became friends with a schoolmate. Cathy Hansen was the daughter of a professor at the university. The girls did their homework together, played together, and enjoyed each other's company. This delighted us—Veronika's happiness increased our own.

Adaptation to American food was another challenge. Jarda and I had experienced a similar problem, although an adult palate usually spans a wider range than a child's. About the only American dish Veronika would eat was Kentucky Fried Chicken. Even ice cream didn't appeal to her because of the slightly salty taste. It was different than the ice cream served in Europe. She eventually became a fan of Howard Johnson's, however, and reveled in the fact that the restaurant chain offered more than thirty different flavors.

Veronika prided herself in being the family ice cream expert. Whenever we traveled and she spotted the orange roof of a Howard Johnson's, she insisted we stop. I was willing to swim across a dangerous channel, hike through the Alps, jump off a moving train, and climb a barbed wire fence for my daughter. Surely, I could stop at HoJo's.

We often traveled to New York to visit friends. The Gallo's were relatives of my cousin Barbara, and they were pleasant, unassuming people. Joe Gallo worked as a window arranger in garment stores and played the saxophone in a jazz orchestra on the weekend. His wife, Bubbles, was a homemaker. A heavy-set woman with an easy disposition and a kind heart, she used makeup in a way that gave her the appearance of a stage actress. The Gallo's lived in the Italian part of Brooklyn with Joe's mother and his special needs sister.

At the Gallo's house, we always felt welcomed and accepted. They reminded us of our own family back home. That was important to us and helped quell the yearning we had for a sense of belonging. They became our extended family in America.

Joe and Bubbles had three children, Jody, Greg, and Valery. Jody managed a card store. She smoked heavily and died of cancer in her 30s. Greg married his high school sweetheart, but they soon divorced. Valery married a widower and they adopted three children to make a happy family. Families in America are not so different from families in Europe.

We had been a family in Czechoslovakia. Then we were separated for two and a half long years. Now we were a family in America.

We set out to find and live the American Dream.

Chapter Nineteen

LESSINA

I remembered Veronika's wish list when we left her in Týniště: she wanted a house, a puppy, and a baby. We leased a small house on the outskirts of State College in preparation for her arrival. One of our neighbors found a loose dog on the street. The black and white collie was only a few weeks old. We named him Lassie, after the movie dog as popular in Czechoslovakia as in America. When we found out the TV Lassie was female, we changed our dog's name to the Czech sounding Lessina.

We didn't provide a baby, but Lessina filled the role of our second child and served as Veronika's brother. He was equally responsive to Czech and English commands, and he loved to be independent. Jarda built a nice doghouse which Lessina largely ignored, except to sit on the roof and nibble at it. He eventually chewed it to destruction.

We guessed he had been born in the beginning of July so, to make the day a really big one, we settled on the Fourth of July as his birthday. Every year thereafter, Lessina got a cake, which he preferred with whipped cream topping, and a gift of a *panenka* —the Czech name for a chewable toy.

When we asked Lessina, "Where is your *panenka*?" he would wag his tail and run off to look for it. He would toss it in the air and catch it again. On the days he favored us, he would let us take it from him. With all that wear and tear, he would always need a new one by his next birthday.

Lessina grew into a handsome dog. When riding in the car with us, he preferred the seat next to the driver. While waiting for me to come out of a store, he would repeatedly leap about the car, seeking an opening so he could survey the area for action. Or he would sit in the driver's seat as if he deserved it.

Once, while I was on my way home from the store, I glanced in the mirror and wondered why a dog was madly racing behind my car. It was Lessina, of course. He had jumped through a half-open car window and I had left him behind in the parking lot!

Dog trainers tell you that when a dog misbehaves, you should give him a gentle whack. When Lessina misbehaved, he was intelligent enough to quickly present a pitiful sight, offering his paw to make peace, and looking like he felt sorry for himself. This trick worked well enough that he usually escaped with just a verbal chastisement.

He showed his affection by licking my face. Since I'd never had a dog as a child, I was not fond of this. When I asked the veterinarian about it, he assured me the act was far less dangerous than it would have been if it were the other way around.

As is common among canines, Lessina frequently fell in love with a lady dog in the neighborhood and wandered off. Our telephone number on his collar helped alert us where to find him. Usually he could be found sitting in front of his beloved's house. As soon as he spotted our car approaching or heard Jarda's whistle, he raced to beat us home and feigned surprise at the fuss when we arrived. However, Lessina did not always get away with such escapades and sometimes fell into the dogcatcher's hands, which cost us a fine and an apology.

I'm not sure why I defied the authorities and continued to let Lessina run free after dark. Maybe I was projecting my own experiences under Nazi and Communist control, but I believed all God's creatures were entitled to a life of their own. Usually Lessina returned before we retired or sometime during the night. Sometimes he would be covered with mud or infested with ticks, which I removed with forceps.

Unfortunately, he also had two significant collisions with cars. The first was while chasing a rabbit in front of our house and the accident was relatively minor. But, after the second collision, the driver of the car brought Lessina to us in the middle of the night. The dog was unconscious and wrapped in a blanket.

Lessina survived the night, and in the morning was his usual affectionate self.

Through all of his 16 years, Lessina behaved like a champ. He was a member of our family and our love and respect for each other was mutual. I think Lessina thought of himself as human, and in many ways, he was like one. When confronted with a relationship problem, I often wondered how Lessina would go about it.

It was hard to watch his days drawing to an end, his apologetic expression when he was no longer able to control his bodily functions. Death came in a way that was as heroic as his life. Lessina was resting in the driveway when another dog entered the premises in pursuit of a female who had also aroused Lessina's interest. When Lessina challenged the other dog, the stress to his feeble body resulted in a heart attack. He was in a coma when I found him, the lady dog sitting beside him while the other dog watched from a distance. I called

Jarda and Veronika and we agreed to let Lessina die in his sleep.

This happened in the winter. We wished to bury Lessina beneath a flower bed in our garden. Jarda spent several days burning a fire to thaw the frozen ground. The burial was held with full honors. *Panenka* and a favorite bone were laid next to Lessina in the grave.

Lessina will live forever in our hearts. God bless his soul!

Chapter Twenty

PROUD DAYS

Summer 1969:
Three Years of Freedom

Jarda finished his doctoral studies after three years of study, and we invited Grandma Caslavsky to come to the graduation ceremony. Czechoslovakia was now split into the Czech and Slovak Republics and was under the firm control of the Soviets, but to our surprise the Communists let her come to visit. Her first time on an airplane, Grandma flew with Czech Airlines from Prague to New York.

Like us, she arrived on a hot summer day.

We had made reservations at the Stanford Hotel in Manhattan. We were curious to see Grandma's reaction to New York. In Manhattan, she looked around, seemingly unimpressed, and said, "Tell me, how is it possible people do not mind living with so much dirt in the streets? And why are they dressed so shabbily? Don't they care about themselves?"

In State College, Grandma took care of the house and the cooking. She could not speak a word of English, but bravely went about buying groceries in a nearby shop, and she attended church every Sunday, a different church each week. She had heard many stories about strange religious practice in the US and she wanted to form her own opinion. There were enough religious groups in State College that, in the time she spent with us, she did not need to visit any church twice. She always went by herself and came out with a smile, shaking hands with her fellow worshipers. Thus, she became an expert on Catholic, Anglican, Methodist, Baptist, Jewish, and some other religious practices.

Unlike in Europe, the graduation ceremony at Penn State was held in the football stadium. We all dressed for the occasion in distinguished black, with the exception of Veronika who wore a red skirt and white blouse with a ribbon in her light brown hair. She carried a bouquet of flowers for her dad.

Jarda joined the few PhD candidates who, dressed in their doctoral robes, led the graduation procession. We were very proud of him. He had met all the requirements for the geochemistry-material sciences degree in a fine manner. Grandma watched the ceremony through binoculars as we translated the speeches for her. We celebrated afterward with a special dinner and Champagne.

At the end of Veronika's 5th grade school year, we were invited to a play about the Civil War. Veronika and some of her classmates authored the play, and acted in it as well. Veronika's teacher introduced the play by saying, "You may wish to know that one of the co-authors of this play, who also appears in it, came to this school less than ten months ago not knowing a word of English. I challenge the parents in the audience to identify this student."

Veronika spoke with a proper Pennsylvanian accent. Her English was so perfect, no one was able to identify her as the foreign student. I always knew she had an exceptional intellect, but I too was impressed by her skill with the language. Her grandmother, Jarda and I were so proud of her.

Chapter Twenty-One

THE AMERICAN DREAM

1969/1970 School Year:
Veronika's 6th Grade in Boston

It was time to plan our relocation. We wanted to find new jobs and a more permanent home. The US Academy of Sciences in Washington D.C. offered Jarda a stipend to work at the Army Materials and Technology Research Center located in Watertown, Massachusetts. We went to Boston to survey the area and check on available housing.

Our findings were not encouraging. Rents were generally double or triple those in State College. Jarda's scholarship was not very large, which meant I would have to work too. Grandma was leaving for home at the end of the month, so nobody would be at home during the day for Veronika. Also, none of the apartments we looked at allowed pets, and we were certainly not willing to part with Lessina.

We finally found a townhouse we could afford in the suburb of Framingham, one which permitted pets and children. We put down a deposit for September and returned to State College to pack.

We often played bridge during lunch in the lab. One of the players, Dr. Newnham, asked us about our search for housing in Boston. He became thoughtful after we related our experience. Then he suggested we make another trip there and look for a house to buy. He explained that making payments on a mortgage would be preferable to paying a similar amount in rent. This made sense to us, so off we went once more to Boston.

The most attentive of the real estate agents we met was Mr. Hogan in Lexington, Massachusetts, a very nice suburb of Boston. We were interested in Lexington because the public schools there were among the best in the state and, we learned later, among the best in the nation. Mr. Hogan showed the three least expensive houses for sale in town.

The first he showed us was a dilapidated one-bedroom house which would have required extensive and costly repairs. As two PhDs with no fixer-upper experience, we passed on that one.

The second faced a cemetery on a very busy road and had almost no yard. It was a particularly unattractive house and nothing about it caught our eye.

The third house had a lovely garden. All three of us liked the house and the yard, but with a price of $28,000, and with the required 20% down payment on the mortgage, we couldn't afford it.

We returned home, disappointed once more. At noon on Monday, we again sat for bridge with Dr. Newnham. "How was your trip? Did you find something you liked?" he asked.

We told him about the house with the pretty garden, and lamented that it was beyond our means.

"How much more would you need to buy that house?" he asked.

"Close to $4,000," Jarda said.

Dr. Newnham pulled out his checkbook and wrote us a check for $4,000. "Go to Boston and buy the house with the big garden. You can repay me when you're able to do so."

He didn't even want a receipt. He was a nobleman among scientists.

We bought the house and moved to Lexington.

JARDA AND I HAD SURVIVED NAZI AND COMMUNIST occupation. We had succeeded in getting our precious daughter out of Czechoslovakia. My husband had a good job with the Army Material Research Lab. I got a good job with the Forsyth Institute, a dental clinic and research organization. We lived in a beautiful home with a garden in an affluent suburban Boston community. We even had a dog.

We were about to live the American Dream, but almost immediately, our dream turned into a nightmare.

On her first day in school, Veronika got lost on her way home. She was older and more mature than her classmates, and found it impossible to make friends. After that, things went from bad to worse. She became rebellious in school. We began to hear complaints from the administration. Veronika was not fond of her teacher, and the teacher was not fond of her. Her budding adolescence didn't help. It was clear we had a problem.

Veronika proposed a solution. "Send me back to Grandma," she said.

I could barely speak. "What! After all the years of . . . of . . ." I couldn't find the words. I couldn't imagine sending her back there. Yet, nothing hurt me more than seeing my daughter unhappy. I had to find a solution. I sought help and advice everywhere I could.

Opa Leitner had one that sounded like it might work. He suggested we find a European companion around Veronika's age. In fact, he had a friend in Fulda, Germany with a 13-year-old daughter. Opa thought the family might be interested in having her spend some time studying in America. She could come live with us and be a companion for Veronika.

The Mahler family had six children, and they were eager to send their daughter Ilse to stay with us—with one condition: at the end of a year, we would reciprocate by sending Veronika to stay with them and attend the German secondary school in Fulda.

I thought it might be a good idea. Jarda didn't have the same confidence in Opa's solution. Opa had always been like a father to me so I trusted his opinion. Jarda reluctantly agreed to give it a try, and Veronika unenthusiastically said it was okay with her.

1970/1971 School Year:
Veronika's 7th grade

ILSE CAME TO AMERICA AND AT THE BEGINNING OF THE next school year. We enrolled her in school with Veronika. We thought the two girls could go to and from school together, make twice as many friends, and keep each other company at school functions and dances. But this did not happen.

Ilse was entirely unprepared for such a big change in her life. She found speaking English and keeping up in Veronika's school too much of a challenge. Rather than help Veronika make friends, the two became more isolated. As time went on, she became difficult to handle, insisting that everything be done as it was back home in Germany. This was not only impossible, but often incompatible with our own *modus operandi*. Plus, Ilse and Veronika did not get along.

AFTER THREE TRYING MONTHS, I SAT THE GIRLS DOWN AND told them the arrangement had not worked out. They had not become friends and Ilse was not happy living under our roof. I told them I was going to write to Ilse's mother and put an end to the constant bickering by calling off the arrangement.

I was surprised by their reaction. Both girls began to cry. Ilse pleaded that she did not want to return home. Please, please, please could she stay the whole year? Veronika supported her request. She did not want Ilse to leave. Apparently, the girls did care for one another. I thought maybe, with a little effort, we could all get along better.

Our relationships and the girls' behavior did improve after that—not tremendously, but tolerably—and remained this way to the end of the school year. To her surprise, Ilse finished the year with decent grades. She had learned English during her stay, and she matured physically and mentally. We were pleased with her progress.

In July, the girls were scheduled to leave for Germany. Once again, I faced a Sophie's choice: for my daughter's happiness, I had to again let her live apart from us. Veronika wanted to go, and I had made the commitment to the Mahler's. She left for Germany.

I hoped she would fare better in Germany than she had in America.

Chapter Twenty-Two

A CHILD IN GERMANY

1971/72 School Year:
Veronika's 8th Grade

During the first three months, the letters from Mrs. Mahler were similar to the ones I had sent to her the previous year. But this time, she was the one presenting one complaint after another about my daughter's behavior. I wondered if Veronika was resistant to change or if she was simply stubborn and contrary.

When I had my fill of complaints, I wrote to Veronika, telling her to pack up and return home by Christmas. Her reaction was similar to Ilse's the year before: she begged to stay on. The Mahler's allowed her to try again, and the situation improved to a tolerable level.

"*Gott sei Dank!*" Thank God, was Mrs. Mahler's response.

Veronika spoke no German when she moved in with the Mahler family. The German schools are hard, even for German students, and Veronika struggled. As she later explained, she had to memorize her lessons in order to get a passing grade. There were problems with English as well as her teacher insisted on British pronunciation and spelling.

At the end of the school year, Veronika was included in a group selected to represent the school in a national math competition. We were proud of her. Her German had improved so that she spoke like a native, another success for which we praised her.

By the end of the school year I had accumulated ten weeks of vacation, which had to be used, or it would be forfeited. I wanted to travel to Germany to pick up Veronika, and I thought we might travel around Europe together. Jarda didn't have that much time off, so we decided I would go without him.

Veronika asked if she could stay for the summer with the friends she had made. I said yes, I would take a vacation in Europe before picking her up in Germany.

I bought a railroad pass and traveled extensively throughout Europe, visiting all the places I had always wished to see. It was like a dream come true. I landed in London, took the ferry to France, went to Portugal, Spain, Italy, and finally, via Switzerland, to Germany and Fulda.

Some moments of that trip were unforgettable.

While walking on a glacier in the Alps, I heard a children's choir singing songs from *The Sound of Music*. Were my ears deceiving me? No, the voices were those of a Midwestern school choir on vacation in Europe.

Strolling in Lisbon after dark, I again heard a choir. I assumed the voices were coming from a nearby church, so I went to investigate and found the church closed. I then followed the singing to a restaurant garden where the guests were singing to the accompaniment of a guitar. Tile-decorated Lisbon with its narrow alleys, seaport, and gazebos with climbing vines charmed me. The city has a pleasant unpretentious ambience and, foremost, the people possess an unassuming natural grace.

In Italy I succumbed to the beauty of evenings spent in Rome. I didn't like the pomp of the Vatican. On top of Vesuvius, I decided to look for Pompeii without the benefit of a map. Leaving my group and tour guide, I explored the other side of the volcano and descended into what I thought would be Pompeii. To my chagrin, I found a parking lot containing a single Volkswagen Beetle. Before I could start back up the mountain, the owners of the VW returned. The young English couple was on vacation and they were heading to Pompeii. When I explained my predicament, they laughed and offered me a ride.

I spent a very pleasant afternoon with this couple. We explored Pompeii, as well as one of the Greek temples near the seashore. We dined there and swam in the Mediterranean. They dropped me off at the Naples railroad station after I assured them I could safely ride an express train to Rome.

The train was scheduled to arrive in Rome at 1 AM, but I wasn't concerned because my lodging adjoined the railroad station. Once I left the train, however, I realized I was not at the main station but somewhere on the outskirts of Rome— with no taxi in sight.

The people on the train with me dispersed and I was alone at the station with one man. When a car came by to pick him up, I hesitantly approached him to ask for a ride to the main station. It was obvious the driver did not want to make the detour, but they did take me in.

The passenger started to make passes at me and, when I objected, they ordered me out of the car. I found myself on a street in the center of Rome near the Colosseum. I had a vague idea about the direction in which the main station lay as I had been in the area before, so I walked in that direction, hurrying among the prostitutes and stumbling drunks until I recognized the street where my boardinghouse was located on the uppermost floor of an office building. At that hour of the night, the offices were empty.

Just as I turned down the street, I noticed two men following a short distance behind. I assumed they were headed for the railway station. But, to my horror, when I opened the door of the building, they also entered. I pushed the elevator button and they did nothing. I decided should they attack me in the elevator I would pretend to faint and let them take whatever they wished.

We all got on the elevator. I pushed the button for the 5th floor, and again they did nothing. It turned out that one of the men was the son of the proprietor, and he was returning home late with his friend. But the encounter terrified me. When I entered my room, I threw myself on the bed and cried myself to sleep.

With all the glory and majesty of Europe behind me—all the fear and trepidation, the mistakes and the kindnesses of strangers, I headed for Germany to pick up my daughter. I still had about a week left of vacation, and I planned for us to go home through Paris and spend a few days in the City of Lights. *La Ville-Lumière.*

I was not prepared for what happened next.

Veronika refused to go with me. The Mahler's had offered her the option of remaining with them to live as part of their family. Veronika told me she wanted that very much. She was accustomed to the German way of life, which was similar to that of the Czechs, and she had formed an especially close relationship with Ilse's twin sister Charlotte. Also, she had a boyfriend in Fulda.

The Mahler family was large enough so she would never be alone. There were a variety of personalities and ages. At home in

America, she would live as an only child with two parents who worked. She enjoyed the varied interests of the Mahler's and the trips they took to the Alps and the sea. What more could a teenager ask for?

I put my foot down and said I would not leave her there. We would first return to Lexington. If she still wanted to return to Germany, we would talk over the matter with her father. Fortunately, Dr. and Mrs. Mahler backed me up and we left for Paris.

Veronika's mood was such that it would probably have been better to fly home directly from Germany. We lodged in a small hotel in the artist community of Montmartre, from which we made daily excursions. Veronika seemed displeased with everything—Versailles, the Mona Lisa, the old railway station turned into the D'Orsay Museum. When we went looking for the Bastille, we found it was no longer there. In a way, that was a metaphor that applied to Veronika as well.

Finally, it was time for us to go home. Veronika's flight was aboard a commercial airline and mine was the next day on a chartered plane. We arrived at the Orly airport two hours before her scheduled departure. As we approached the escalator taking passengers to customs and the departure gate, Veronika stopped short and looked at me with disdain.

"You're not going to accompany me as far as the gate, are you? Like I'm a baby?" she said with all the assurance of a young woman who knew exactly what she wanted.

I said okay and we parted there. I watched her step on the escalator, rise up and disappear into the airport without looking back. I headed for the airport exit and waited on the sidewalk for the bus back to the city. But when it came, I didn't get on. I walked back and forth for a while, and when I thought Veronika was safely aboard the airplane, I reentered the airport, rode the escalator up, and looked around.

I noticed that passengers with US passports could merely flash it to get past the checkpoint without being stopped or asked to show plane tickets. I did not have a ticket but I had my passport and, imitating those who preceded me, I walked to where the Boston plane was nearly fully boarded.

At the counter, I asked if Veronika was safely on board.

"Oh, Mrs. Caslavsky, I'm so glad you're here. No, your daughter is not on the plane. We've been calling her on the public address system, but she hasn't responded. We will be closing the gate in about 15 minutes."

Now what?

I checked the restrooms, and looked around the duty-free shops. Veronika was nowhere to be seen. I started heading back to the checkpoint to find the police. Just then a door opened at the far end of the hall and out came Veronika, accompanied by a policeman.

She cried out, "Mother, do you have your passport with you?"

"Sure, why?"

"They think I'm a runaway. I have no stamp in my passport to show where and when I entered France and they want to know why!"

Veronika had been asleep when we entered France from Germany on the train. The immigration officer was satisfied to see my passport in which Veronika was listed as my child, and he did not stamp her passport.

The police held up the plane's departure, and Veronika boarded at last.

That night, my last in Paris, an old but close family friend came from London to wish me Godspeed. Oscar Rodan was a Czech Jew who escaped Nazi occupation in 1939. He got as far as Shanghai, where his first job was selling matches and laces on the street. But he'd ended up a successful businessman in London.

Oscar and I had dinner in a Latin Quarter nightclub. We had a good time, as was always the case with Oscar. He presented me with a gift, of a bottle of Chanel No. 5. For that one night, I was able to forget my troubles with Veronika.

The next morning, I boarded the plane to Boston. I sat alone with my thoughts. What had I done? I'd worked so hard to get my daughter back, only to send her away again. Now she wanted to stay away, and live in Germany. In a few hours, I would face an unhappy daughter and a husband who would surely be displeased with the turn of events.

Chapter Twenty-Three
VERONIKA'S CHOICE

Veronika's High School through College

Back at home, the situation with Veronika was difficult. We discussed the issue over and over again. She wanted to return to her friends in Germany. We wanted her to stay with us in Lexington.

Jarda and I could understand her feelings, but we tried to explain to her that, at 15 going on 16, separation from us would virtually put an end to our life together as a family. She would essentially become a member of the Mahler family.

She argued that she hated the school and the kids in Lexington. Her real friends were in Fulda and, no matter where she lived, she would still be a member of our family. After all, hadn't she shown that already? She was always a precocious child, and even as a little girl, opinionated and set in her ways. I think she inherited those traits from me.

We tried to convince her to at least finish high school in America. We told her that at that point she would be an adult and free to choose to live wherever she wanted. The decision would be hers and hers alone. We would not interfere once she turned 18.

Jarda and I both felt strongly that Veronika's life was hers to live—me a little more with my liberal *Gymnázium* education, Jarda a little less with his black-and-white Technical School education. We told her we thought she should stay with us, but in the end, we left the decision to her.

After struggling with this burden, Veronika agreed to stay with us. But it was obvious from the beginning of the 1972/1973 school year that she was not happy. I frequently regretted we had lobbied so hard to hold her back. I never wanted her to feel forced to do something or to be unhappy—and she was indeed unhappy.

This depressed me and I could feel the ghost of my mother's temperament haunting me. The resulting milieu affected our family life, but somehow, we went on.

About six months into the school year, a young man named Adam arrived at the front door. He introduced himself and said he was there to take Veronika out on a date. We were surprised when he inquired whether we would be bothered by the fact that he was a Jew. He clearly didn't understand us or our experience.

In Czechoslovakia, we had been accustomed to easy relations with other religions and nationalities. Oscar Rodan's sister, Mrs. Alice Wagner, was a Jew and she lived as a tenant in Grandfather Kudrnka's house. As a little girl, I often visited her. She had no children and played games with me. She was my favorite adult friend. My parents and grandparents let me continue to visit her after the Nazis forced her to wear a yellow star and all contact with Jews was forbidden. Mrs. Wagner survived the war, but her mother perished in the Osvietim concentration camp.

It didn't take Adam long to figure out that we weren't the

kind of people that held prejudices and that Veronika wasn't the kind of girl that asked permission from her parents before she did something. The two of them began a relationship that lasted through high school.

Adam also studied drums at the Boston Conservatory of Music. Veronika once told me that she and Adam were viewed as an ideal couple at their school. We enjoyed a good relationship with Adam's parents, gentle, well-educated people with a liberal bent.

After graduating from high school, Veronika enrolled at Wellesley College, one of the best liberal arts colleges in the country. Adam and Veronika got engaged and for a year lived together in an apartment in Boston. Once, in the spring, we all traveled to Florida for a brief vacation.

Unfortunately, Adam became ill with a fever. Despite being fed chicken soup, which he called "Jewish penicillin," his condition deteriorated. After calling and consulting with his parents, we took him to the emergency room of a local hospital.

He came out from his examination visibly shaken. The doctors told him he indeed had the flu, but they also diagnosed a more serious disease. We were all in shock. It wasn't until we got back to Boston and he got a full medical work up that we found out the Florida doctors had misdiagnosed him. It had not been what you would call a pleasant vacation.

Some of our friends wondered why Adam and Veronika were allowed to live together without being married. Maybe it went back to our obsession with freedom. We did not feel it was our decision to make, nor were we unmindful of our own passionate love affair in our youth.

Veronika's romance with Adam ended the next summer. Adam joined a jazz band on a cruise ship, and he failed to write to her for two months. She decided on her own that this might be the pattern for the rest of their lives.

Veronika had inherited her father's independent spirit.

I kept in touch with Adam's parents for several years. Adam changed his college major from liberal arts to psychology. His parents divorced and he became a psychologist. He moved to North Carolina, married, and last I heard, was expecting his first child. I always wished him and his family all the best.

In her sophomore year, Veronika moved into a tower dorm with another girl. When she had settled in her room, she invited us to see it. We reciprocated by offering to take her to dinner. She was sorry, she said, but she had to decline as she had a meeting to attend.

"We have to decide some important issues. There is this matter of guidelines for men visiting us in the dorm. You know, like how many nights they can stay, what utilities they may share with us, the showers, and things like that."

Obviously, such issues were important and not to be taken lightly at an all-female college.

One Sunday morning, we visited the girls and brought them a basket of apples. Veronika met us at the outside gate and invited us to her room. She knocked and entered with us behind her. The girls shared a bunk bed, Veronika had the bottom bunk, her roommate the top. A young man was sleeping in Veronika's bunk.

"Who is that boy?" I asked her.

"I don't know," Veronika replied. "He was already here, sleeping on the floor when I came home last night. After I woke up this morning, I told him to move to my bed where he would be more comfortable."

One should never jump to conclusions before knowing all the facts.

Veronika was studying German and Spanish literature. Initially, we had been ambivalent about her choices. In our view, the study of languages wouldn't lead to a good career. She thought she might go into teaching or foreign service.

Since outside influences had forced me to change my career choice from my passion for medicine, I had a lot of sympathy for Veronika and wished for her to make her own choice. Jarda certainly felt that way as well. We agreed it was Veronika's decision to make, and we believed that if you were proficient in your chosen line of work, you would eventually be recognized and rewarded.

Veronika was an attractive girl. At Wellesley, she dated a few MIT students, and might have had a brief, clandestine relationship with one of the young instructors at the college. She graduated in 1980.

After graduating from Wellesley, she received a scholarship to the university in Bonn, and she finally returned to Germany. There she dated a student from Wisconsin, but the relationship ended soon after their return to the US.

After that, Veronika told us she wanted to spend the rest of her life alone.

I lamented this idea and wondered if all that I had put her through—the long separation, followed by the forced stay in the US—would ultimately ruin her life. Jarda thought she was just reacting to the emotional hurt of the breakup. But her unhappiness evoked a sadness in me. I had broken free from the Nazis and the Communists who occupied my country, but not from the melancholy that occupied my mind.

Chapter Twenty-Four

A DECADE IN-BETWEEN

1980–1990

Now that Veronika had graduated from college and was living on her own, Jarda and I settled into living our own lives. We went to work every day, and got together with friends and acquaintances on weekends. If we met people we liked or wanted to get to know, we invited them to our home. Likewise, for people we wanted to help. The decade seemed to fly by.

All through the 1980s, I continued to work at the Forsyth Institute in Boston. One of my colleagues was Tian-jia, who was on an exchange program from a dental institute in China. She was a very kind woman, all alone in this country. Jarda and I sort of adopted her as our friend. Jarda picked her up on the weekends and brought her to our house. We became very close over the few years she was here.

In the fall of 1988, I was invited to present a series of seminars at the West China Medical University Dental School. I wasn't sure, but I suspected Tian-jia had something to do with this invitation.

The Chinese made every effort to make my stay pleasant. A bacteriologist befriended me and loaned me her bicycle so that I could join the millions of Chinese riding on the streets. I also had a personal guide who, I suspect, was a police agent.

When I had finished my lectures, the dean of the school asked what she could do to reciprocate. I told her I would like to visit Tibet. The next day, she informed me that a trip to Lhasa would cost me between three to five hundred US dollars per day. That was more than I could afford, and I regretfully apologized for not being able to accept the offer.

On the following day, the dean approached me again. "Would you be interested to go to Tibet traveling as one of us? That is, Chinese, not American?" she asked me.

"Of course I'm interested. But what would this cost?" I asked.

"Not expensive," she said. "Perhaps five or ten US dollars a day. You will travel in a group by bus. It is a charter filled with workers from a factory in Shanghai. The trip is their vacation and reward for distinguished work performance."

She said it would be a good idea to take one of their colleagues with me as companion and interpreter. I invited my friend the bacteriologist to accompany me, but she could not free herself from her teaching duties at the university. Instead, another young female dentist agreed to go. The following morning, we boarded the bus to Tibet.

The bus left Chengdu station at 6 AM. We passed through forests inhabited by pandas, and small villages and towns where we would occasionally pause for a rest stop or a meal.

At night we slept in hostels in Chinese communes. These

places were like a cross between army barracks and a fort. There was no heat in the buildings even though it was the end of October. For the most part, the beds were covered with not very clean linens and the only "luxury" we experienced was that sometimes we had warm water for the basin they gave us on arrival. Breakfast was included and usually consisted of boiled cabbage in a tasteless, hot water soup. Worst of all were the toilets—simple holes in the ground located in dilapidated buildings outside where we slept.

For some reason, my companion barricaded our door with a table or some other heavy object each night before we went to sleep. I did not know the reason for her fear. The other people on the bus seemed peaceful and friendly.

The mountains and valleys steepened as we approached Tibet. Wild rivers flowed far below. Here and there, hanging bridges with missing slats in the walkways connected two sides of a valley. We passed unplanned dams formed by earthquake-induced rockslides, and in one case by a logging truck that did not reach its destination.

Our bus driver appeared to be a genius who saved our lives on more than one occasion. He navigated the bus perfectly along the narrow roads. Sometimes he seemed to drive with uncanny accuracy within an inch of road's edge.

In one Tibetan village, a rogue cracked the windshield with a stone. Evidently the Chinese were not welcome in Tibet.

The region we visited appeared to be medieval. The doors of the houses had signs to pacify or ward off evil spirits. Only the women worked in the fields. A woman who allowed me to photograph her was immediately chastised and then struck by a man.

The villages resembled fortresses surrounded by high fences with Tibetan flags at the gates. Some buildings were beautifully carved. Evening meals were often prepared on open fires. One evening we sang songs and danced after the meal.

We arrived at a place in the mountains where the river formed numerous waterfalls and gorges, carved formations in the sandstone, and made pools of dark blue with green tints. The scenery was so beautiful we didn't want to leave. Unfortunately, we had to cut the trip short because an approaching snowfall threatened to close the road.

During the trip back, I became ill. The other passengers on the bus gave me clothes so I could keep warm. Several shared herbal medicines, while others offered whatever sweets or other treats they carried with them from home. I will always remember the people on the bus with gratitude.

On our return to Chengdu, my condition worsened and I had developed a painful ear infection. I declined hospitalization as proposed by the university people as I feared I might contact a viral or bacterial infection there.

Instead, I slept in clean linens in the clean room that was designated for foreigners on campus. The rooms were entered from a courtyard with a gate that was guarded and likely under around-the-clock surveillance.

At the same compound was a young Midwestern couple who had volunteered to teach English. Their initial enthusiasm about the work had faded by the time I met them, and they were quite critical of the conditions in the English department. They disliked the rigid rules and the unwillingness of their hosts and colleagues to try modern teaching methods. They wanted to terminate their contract and return home.

During my illness, I stayed warm and drank plenty of tea. My friend Tian-jia visited me daily, bringing me homemade meals. Another elderly professor came regularly with fresh flow-ers. He told me stories about his youth and the conditions at the university when it was still a missionary school. As a farewell present, he gave me an album with photos of the region's curiosities. Some I had visited on my bus tour and some he had gone to visit in his youth.

Ethnically, the Chinese people could not be more unlike the Czech people, yet they displayed the same kindness and willingness to care for strangers. Like the Czechs, they were a peaceful and loving people. Somehow, they had found themselves in the same predicament as the Czech people—totally under the control of their Communist government. I felt a kinship with these good people.

As soon as I was well enough to stay on my feet, I left Chengdu. I flew home by way of Hong Kong. My illness persisted and, by time I got to Lexington, I was so sick that Jarda worried about my survival.

He got me immediate medical attention. I have to say, the Western antibiotics succeeded where tea, soup, and Eastern herbal remedies had failed.

"*Gott sei Dank!*" as Mrs. Mahler would say.

Chapter Twenty-Five

I AM GOING HOME

hortly after I got back from China, Czechoslovakia underwent some major changes.

In November, a student demonstration in Prague was suppressed by the riot police of the Communist government. The day of the demonstration marked the 50th year anniversary of a demonstration against Nazi occupation. The student demonstrators were joined by older dissidents and the crowds swelled to over half a million.

This led to street demonstrations all over Czechoslovakia, followed by a general strike that finally forced the resignation of the Communist government. A non-Communist government was installed and the barbed wire barriers were removed from the borders with West Germany and Austria.

In June of 1990, Czechoslovakia held free and democratic elections for the first time since 1946. My homeland was free, and for the first time in decades, we could return without fear of reprisal.

The Czech Republic was my home, and my home was always

in my heart. For years, I had wanted return there, to visit the place of my birth, the homes of my grandparents, the places we lived and worked in Prague. Jarda and I talked about it, but he still harbored anger about the way the country had treated us. He wasn't ready to return, but he told me if I wanted to go, I should go. I thought it over and made a decision.

After 25 years of exile, I was going home. My parents and grandparents were gone, but I still had relatives and friends there.

When Veronika arrived in America on August 13, 1968, we had appeared on the local television news. The reporter asked us the reason for leaving our native country. My answer was we left because we desired to live in a free society. In addition to the overwhelming Communist government control, my husband Jarda's life was in constant danger.

I decided after that television interview that I would someday write the story of what really happened. Our relatives and friends, with one or two exceptions, had not been informed about the dangers we faced when we were there. Because we had to operate in secrecy, they had no idea why we'd left. All they knew was one day we were gone.

Now that I was planning to go home, I lamented never having written that story.

My trip was going to last only seven days. I planned to visit those places especially dear to my heart. I would land in Prague where Jarda and I started our married life and my daughter was born. I would visit my hometown of Chrudim where I spent my childhood with my parents and loving Novak and Kudrnka grandparents. I wanted to visit Jarda's hometown of Týniště nad Orlici, and the town of Liberec where my Aunt Eva lived and Jarda and I first met. My last stop would be our little cottage at Krizanovice where the river that runs through Chrudim is dammed to create a gorgeous reservoir.

I made plans to meet my friends, schoolmates, and remaining members of the family including the many children I had never seen before. The thought occurred to me that, in addition to candy or souvenir trinkets, I should give them something substantial.

I decided to write the account of our lives from the time we left Czechoslovakia in 1965. My story would contain all of the things they didn't know and would surely ask me about. I didn't want our story and the story of our country to become part of the forgotten past. I would make sure that didn't happen.

Right before my trip, I worked on the manuscript. I wrote for five days and nights, recording all the facts as I remembered them. The report ended up being a 30-page monograph I called, "25 Years in Exile." I made copies and brought them with me to the Czech Republic.

UNTIL I RETURNED HOME, I HAD NOT REALIZED THE extent to which I had been suppressing my feelings—not only of loss and sadness, but also anger. I always held the land of my birth close to my heart. I felt nostalgia and homesickness for the places I had grown up, gone to school, and lived. I needed to visit those places to work my way through all the suppressed memories and associated emotions.

I was at my father's grave in Chrudim when the first memories came roaring back. The overwhelming grief of losing him at a time in my life when a girl needs her father most—as she starts to become a young woman. It's a time when she tries on an adult mantle knowing she can slip back into little girl with her father's protection. That security had been taken from me, and on top of that, I was called on to make the momentous decision of stopping the life of the unborn child in my mother's womb.

I realized how all my life I had tried so hard to understand my mother's moods and her illness. I was never able to do so. There by her grave in Chrudim, I talked to her and came to peace with all that had happened between us. She was a good woman tormented by her own demons. A smart young woman who spoke English, German, and Czech, but who never reached her potential. A poor soul beaten down by the cruelty of war, who retreated into her own little world rather than accept the one in which she lived. I regretted that she'd died alone in Chrudim, and I told her how sorry I was about that.

When I visited my grandparents' homes in Chrudim, I was soothed by the memories of the unconditional love I received from them. There is nothing more precious to a little girl than to be adored by a grandfather and to be in his constant company. Grandpa Kudrnka did that for me. Grandpa Novak told me stories and taught me to play violin. My grandmothers cared for me and taught me many lessons that I relied on time and time again in my life.

At the root of depression is anger. When I stood at the grave of Grandpa Kudrnka, the sorrow felt so heavy in my gut. It got heavier and heavier. The next thing I knew, a burst of anger erupted in me, as if a boulder had broken through the floor of my being and splashed into a pool of vile liquid. What came up in my mind was hatred. Hatred for the murderers who killed Grandpa Kudrnka in prison, hatred for the bureaucrats of the Socialist medical system who failed Grandpa Novak, hatred for the occupiers who persecuted my husband, hatred for the petty communist officials who kept my daughter from me for so long.

The found hatreds passed through me like giant waves. One moment I was calm, remembering the love I once received in a place I visited. The next moment I felt the swell of intense grief from the loss of that love. Finally, I felt the crash of anger toward those who had wronged us. The feelings swirled together inside me. I cried and cried. Then the feelings were gone.

I was glad that on my first trip back to my homeland, I had traveled alone. I didn't want anyone to see all those emotions erupting, and I didn't want anyone to stop them from coming out of me.

Both the English and Czech languages have one word for tears, but there should be three. Tears of joy are different from tears of sorrow, and they are different from tears of rage.

Once the storms of emotion had passed and the tears had finished raining down, I was left with a feeling of peace and gratitude. The feelings I will never again suppress are the deep love I have for the town and country of my birth and for those who raised me—and loved me—and made me into a God-obeying human being.

Recently I discovered among my mementos of the past the following poem, which was written by a fellow high-school student for me and perhaps about me. What amazes me today is how accurate he was in his fortunetelling.

A Girl's Song

Destinies flow from within me
To face blizzards and gales.

I feel so helpless
Not being able
To prevent collisions
Of their prows.

The Pilot unseen
Yet controls
The lifeboat
In which I try to escape.

The mad torrent
Comes from my heart
And threatens to hurtle
My own fate
Into the waves…

"There is no life without dreams and love.
Without love and dreams poets cannot exist."

—by Emil Minar
Serak, Czech Republic
January 22, 1951
(Translation by S. Lukes)

Chapter Twenty-Six

A LAST HURRAH

After 20 successful years of working at the Forsyth Institute, my grant and financial support dried up. I'm not sure I minded that much. I was 58 years old, my daughter was on her own, and I had already made the return to my home country. I was a little depressed and I was tired of working.

Jarda was still two years away from retirement, however, so I did not feel right about not working. A colleague in Germany wanted me to come work in his department, where they were using one of the most advanced analytical techniques of the time. I was familiar with their work through the technical literature and it sounded interesting, but I wasn't sure I wanted to make the commitment.

Jarda and I discussed being apart for a couple years. We were adult about it, as we knew it wouldn't affect our marriage. We had talked about eventually retiring to Florida, so the extra money could make help make this possible. When I returned from Germany, we could retire at the same time.

The man who offered me the job was persistent. Jarda encouraged me to accept the position, so I finally agreed to work there for a period of two years. I left for Germany, oddly enough, following in my daughter's footsteps.

I had mixed feelings about the Germans. I could not forget the past, but I also did not want to blame the young Germans for past injustices. I wanted to get to know the contemporary Germans and base my opinions on that.

I found cultured, sophisticated, and knowledgeable people who were fond of art, music, and their work. People like my good friend Ursula, a school director who was honest, forthright, caring, and independent-minded. But there were others like my cheating landlord, a pompous man of unwarranted pretentiousness. The Germans had a word for him: *untermensch*, which means subhuman creature.

I preferred to associate with the young people who were loyal to their country but not chauvinistic. They were bright, mostly honest, friendly, and pleasant to work with. The women were businesslike, decent, and typically hard workers. But I had a problem with the man who had invited me to work with him.

In my first year there, I became an uncomfortable liability to the man who hired me. He wanted to use my expertise but take all the credit for himself. I wouldn't have it.

Unable to resolve our dispute, I left the job and returned to America. My working days were over.

Chapter Twenty-Seven

OUR WORK IS DONE

Veronika worked in Boston. She met a nice young man from France. They fell in love and got married. She began her journey as a wife, eventually becoming a mother and ultimately her own person living her own life—just as I had always wanted.

Jarda and I were delighted she'd married a good and decent man, but we had one fear. What if he moved his family to France? I did not want my daughter to again live 3000 miles away. Jarda and I suggested they should look into living in the French-speaking region of Canada.

They eventually moved to Quebec, only about 300 miles north of Boston. They had three children—two they birthed and one they adopted, from Mexico.

In March of 1993, Jarda and I retired. We were not wealthy, but we could live comfortably on what we had. Jarda had always loved Florida. We sold our house in Lexington and moved to Pompano Beach on the gold coast of Florida. Our condo over-looks a blue-water pool and the gorgeous white sand beach.

I went swimming in the pool every day. Jarda opted to cross 50 yards of sand to swim in the warm waters of the Atlantic Ocean. He set up a desk/workbench next to floor-to-ceiling windows that overlooked the beach. There he would putter with electronics, batteries, or whatever else intrigued him at the time.

I practiced my photography and decorated the condo with a few keepsakes, like a photograph of the church in Koçi where Grandpa Kudrnka was baptized and the mountains in Slovenia where Jarda and I once skied.

I had a friend in the Czech Republic who restored 14th and 15th century castles. She sent us replicas of the tiles from one of the palaces she worked on, so I used a dozen of them to adorn one wall. Jarda liked a couple of paintings reminiscent of home. One was a rural scene and the other a village. The latter was mounted in a case containing a clock and a mechanical device that played music. Jarda converted it to run on electricity, and we hung it in our living room. I hung a Caslavsky knight in shining armor where I could see it every day.

We met a number of good friends in Florida and frequently hosted late afternoon get-togethers with wine and cheese.

With the money we had left over from the sale of our Lexington house, we bought a house in St Laurent, near Veronika and her family. We spent our summers there and visited with them on holidays. Fifty years and 3 thousand miles away from the Czech Republic, life now had similarities to my childhood in Chrudim with grandparents, parents, and children together on the holidays. We lived happily in this manner.

BUT LIFE AND AGING IN PARTICULAR BRING PROBLEMS regardless of the country where we reside. Not only does our health deteriorate, but certain of our personality traits become more prominent with age. I never lost my need to resist pressure or injustice. Jarda never lost his anger against the Communists. We tried to deal with these problems, occasionally drifting apart, yet always drawn back together in a quest for peace and love.

In 2010, Jarda was involved in a serious car accident. In the months it took him to heal, he experienced several post-traumatic stress attacks. Then something went terribly wrong. A blood clot in his brain caused a stroke that left him physically impaired. His speech, too, was impaired. He became a shadow of the man he had once been.

It was difficult for me to accept the enormity of his disability. I still saw him as the athlete who won medals skiing slalom in the Krkonoše Mountains of the Czech Republic, the young boyfriend who made love to me on the banks of the Labe River, the father who carried his little girl on his shoulders, the man of strength who led me 3000 miles to a new life in America.

The reality was the man I loved was now trapped inside a severely constrained body. He worked hard and he did improve, but from this physical prison there seemed to be no escape.

I cared for him around the clock, helping him in and out of bed, assisting in the bathroom, and cutting up his food. Sometimes he could feed himself, other times he would lose concentration and I would have to help. If he fell, I would recruit a neighbor to help me get him up again. When I saw him sit for hours at his workbench, staring at his batteries without doing anything, I cried.

I tried to make life as normal as possible. I invited sympathetic friends over for dinner, especially those with a scientific bent who could converse on technical subjects. These kind people appreciated Jarda's accomplishments, his intellect, and his skills at his crafts.

On one occasion, I set a Jell-O mold that was to be desert on the table while I went out to the kitchen to get dishes. Much to my chagrin, when I returned I found him eating the Jell-O out of the mold with a spoon. Our good friends laughed, then ate the portions I served to them.

I took him with me when I went food shopping. We'd take his walker out of the trunk of the car, and he would shuffle beside me down the supermarket aisles. What had normally been a 15-minute task became a several-hour-long expedition.

At one point, we found ourselves with an immediate need for a new car. I took Jarda to an auto dealership, where he participated in every step up to and including negotiating the price. When I saw he was exhausted, I told the salesman we had to go. The man allowed me to sign the unprepared documents so we could take our new car home, promising he would fill in the details and mail them to us. I thanked him for his patience and kindness.

When I received the paperwork, however, I found he had charged us the list price, not the one we had negotiated. A friend went to the dealership to ask them to fix this error, but they refused. I had fought against the Nazis and the Communists, but it was a testament to how tired I was that I did not choose to fight the unscrupulous auto dealership.

Although Jarda worked hard to regain his strength and his faculties, his condition worsened. After numerous medical tests, we learned he had cancer. My job became making whatever time he had left as good as possible.

THAT SUMMER I TOOK MY DAUGHTER AND HER FAMILY TO the Czech Republic. We traveled north to Sněžka in the Krkonoše Mountains, where Jarda and I had skied in our early days together and where he had returned many times to ski alone. Several cousins from the Czech Republic joined us there.

We formed a semi-circle on the side of the mountain. I gave each of our grandchildren a bowl containing Jarda's ashes. I asked the children to scatter them deep in a nearby clutch of tall grass. And I told them their grandfather would come back as a tree and live forever on the side of that mountain.

There's an old Czech legend about the spirit *Krakonos* who haunts those mountains. He is friendly and helpful to good people, and vengeful to those who mock him. I believe Jarda's spirit now lives in the mountains with *Krakonos*. They are both vengeful toward all who would harm the innocent. Jarda and *Krakonos* are great friends, and they ski the slopes together— forever free.

Chapter Twenty-Eight

FRANTIŠEK

I spent the next year of my life in a daze. My daughter wanted me to move to Canada, but I felt my home was in Florida. However, being alone at the age of 77 was not easy. I suffered from severe depression and did not feel like living. My physician, my friends, my daughter, all gave me the same advice: I needed a change of scenery—at least for a while.

My mood was one of acquiescence rather than argument. I phoned my cousin Hana in Prague. We had been like sisters when we were young. She now spent the summers with her grandchildren in a cottage south of Chrudim on the reservoir formed by the Seč Dam on the Chrudimka River, near where we grew up.

"Would it be possible for me to come see you while you spend time in Seč?" I asked her.

"Sure," Hana answered, "and you should stay with us for at least a few weeks."

Hana had always been generous.

My stay at Seč was very pleasant. Just what I needed. Hana's brother lived nearby with his grandchildren, so I felt like I had a family again.

One Sunday, a friend who was also a distant relative came to visit Hana's brother. We met when he came by to say hello to Hana. He joined us for the meal and sat by me. František (Francis in English) was very interested in any firsthand news I might have about America.

"What's it like living there?" he asked me.

It took me a while to respond. I told him about the people, the work, the countryside. I told him how much I liked all of it.

"What don't you like?" he asked.

I told him how every once in a while, I see signs of racism. Europe appeared to be better than the US regarding racial tolerance. I said how I was baffled on occasion by some of the political decisions, and I waxed on about the polarization in American politics. It was frustrating to watch politicians take on a difficult issue, and then be unable to find a compromise or to make a decision.

František was once mayor of his small town, so he said that was a universal malady.

He listened intently, asking questions and making small comments to support the things I said. He seemed especially interested how the US economy was doing. He had been an economist and worked for a large oil company in Czechoslovakia.

He told me his story. His parents were farmers in Zaječice, a village not too far from Seč. They raised their son to be an upright, sincere, and honest human being. When he was in his late 20s, František married a local girl. They raised three children. Years later, they were blessed with several grandchildren, then great-grandchildren.

A tall, distinguished-looking man, František was 88 years

old. He had been a widower for 12 years. It was clear he understood and had great empathy for the situation in which I found myself. That alone was very comforting.

Sitting around the table full of people, František seemed uneasy, a bit shy and awkward. When he spoke, however, he did so with authority. But he seldom spoke. He had a sound mind, for his judgment on aspects of our conversation was always precise and clear.

He told me he painted. He called it a hobby, but when I saw some of his work at my cousin's, I called it a passion. His paintings were very expressive and quite good. I especially liked his visions of the countryside and the mountains and his leaning toward abstraction.

When our evening was at an end, Hana and I walked our guests to the door. I opened it and extended my hand to František. He seemed flustered by that, so I retracted it. Then he extended his and quickly retracted it.

I responded by rising on the tips of my toes and giving him a peck on the cheek. He seemed startled and quickly departed. A kiss on both cheeks would have been an appropriate European goodbye. A kiss on one cheek was an American hello.

I thought, "You had better go after him and apologize!"

But before I did so, he turned around and asked, "Would you like to go for a walk with me tomorrow morning?"

I smiled. "Yes, that would be nice."

Thus, began our special friendship. Over the next few days, we walked around the beautiful reservoir at Seč and our friendship deepened into a close relationship. In the years to come, the relationship became filled with love.

THE BEST WAY TO DESCRIBE OUR RELATIONSHIP WAS THIS: IT

was very nice and very respectful. I loved his art, and he liked that I loved it. We never argued—there just never seemed to be anything to argue about. I found this to be unbelievable!

The following winter, František came to visit me in Florida and stayed for three months. He painted by the ocean and collected seashells from which he made beautiful collages.

Then I went to the village of Zaječice to live with him in his apartment at his parents' house. I stayed for six months. Because František had been mayor of Zaječice, everybody knew him and it seemed that all 1200 residents knew me as well.

In the village, most people used bicycles for local travel and cars for longer distances. I had given up driving at the age of 80 when I felt my reactions to the traffic were too slow. In Zaječice, I could walk to do my shopping. For longer excursions, the train station was only 500 yards away from the house. The daily walks were not only healthy, but also therapeutic. I enjoyed the greetings I received from the people and I liked strolling in the countryside.

We went twice to the Alps in Austria, and to various towns and mountains in the Czech Republic. I used to ski in the mountains with my parents and later with Jarda. We also passed near the Krkonoše Mountains between the Czech Republic and Poland, where Jarda's ashes were scattered.

We continued visiting one another in this manner for several years, a few winter months in Florida, a few summer months in Zaječice. In December of 2017, Veronika and her family came to Florida to visit for the holidays. František remained in the Czech Republic with his family. Then I stopped hearing from him.

In February I got word he had been found unconscious on the floor of his bedroom in Zaječice. The doctors determined bleeding had taken place in his brain. No one knew whether a fall caused the bleeding or the bleeding caused the fall. The attending physician refused to operate because František was 93 and in a somewhat fragile condition.

He spent two months in the hospital and six weeks in a rehabilitation facility. I arrived in mid-May to find him in a fragile state. We went for daily walks outdoors, gradually increasing the distance. After about three months, he could walk up to a mile with the help of two canes. Visiting family and friends made his mood improve and his self-confidence grew.

At the end of the summer, a good friend of František visited. Soon after she left, he got a headache. He lay down on the bed, and I called his son who lived nearby, asking him to call a doctor. In the meantime, František lost consciousness. Two days later, he died.

I took so many wonderful walks with František. The countryside around Zaječice was absolutely gorgeous. One day when we were together in the Czech Republic, the weather was as sunny as František's mood. He was happy and healthy that day. When we got home, he asked me a flattering question. I gave him a reassuring answer.

That was the last time we made love.

Chapter Twenty-Nine

LIFE, LOVE, AND MY DREAMS

L ife is full of blessings. As a little girl, I learned on afternoon walks with my grandparents to appreciate God's gifts—the fields and forests, the rivers, the air we breathe, the creatures who surround us with nature's symphony.

I savored the bicycle trips I took with my father, where we would cool ourselves by splashing in the pond on hot summer days. Some 80 years later, I swim every day in the Florida sunshine and cool sea breeze, a testament to the continuity of nature in our lives.

When you are born in a place that brings you such gifts, you remember that place your whole life. You hold it close and dear in your heart. The Czech lands occupy a special place in my heart and *má vlast* has become part of my soul.

The very deep love parents and grandparents hold for their children is another of those priceless gifts. I was fortunate enough experience that kind of devotion on a daily basis throughout my young life, and this taught me the true meaning of love. It's natural to love the Czech people and the Czech lands when I relate it to the love I have for my parents and grand-parents.

People I met along the way also knew the meaning of such love. Dear Fanynka cared for me when my mother was ill. My high school teacher Mr. Šada helped me through a difficult time after the death of my father. My Aunt Eva saw to it that the brash young Jarda treat her niece properly.

There are so many others: Mr. V—, who never betrayed Jarda, even after he was tortured; Anneliese and Rudy, who helped us to finally escape; Dr Megla from Corning glass who saved us when we were alone in America; the Christians, who gave us work and took us into their home. The list goes on and on: My surrogate father, Opa; Dr. Roy who brought us to Penn State and made it possible for Jarda to get his doctorate; Mr. D— of the FBI who put us on track to get Veronika back; Mr. Cattell and Senator Clark who helped make that happen; the Gallo's who became our family away from home; and Dr. Newnham, who gave us the money to buy our first house. These people were all angels, and for each one I thank God.

I held on to Grandpa Novak's violin for many years until I finally passed it down to my grandson Matthieu on the occasion of his baptism in France. It is my hope that I have also passed on to my daughter and her children the sense of a parent's uncondi-tional love. Like the rivers in Czech lands, love flows from gener-ation to generation.

God blessed me with an intelligent, loving daughter of whom I am very proud. Veronika is happily married to a good man and works at a computer software company. Her three chil-dren seem to be inseparable from the image I hold of her. It's as if they are all merged into one child who I will love to my dying day.

I have tried to carry the purity of such love with me in all my human relations, not only with my family, but also with friends and with the men in my life. It was easy to do with the good men in my life, harder with those who harmed me and my family.

People say there is evil in the world. Jarda certainly felt that way. He saw everything as black or white. In the Czech Gymnasium Program where I got my education, I learned there are always shades of gray. The German people I met in my life, especially those who cared for my daughter in her teenage years, were good and just, yet the Nazi government committed terrible atrocities. Likewise, I sang songs with the good Russian soldiers who lived in our house and liberated our people in the spring of 1945. Later on, the Communist government became our oppressors.

How could good people go so wrong? There are certainly those who hate and want to do harm, but I believe at the base of such human folly is a feeling of fear—fear of the other. When you think the land and the people you love are most threatened, your fear becomes greatest.

I believe people do what they do to protect what they love more than to take away what others value. I have forgiven the German and Russian people for what was taken from me and my family.

I have traveled over much of the world, and everywhere I have found good people. I was honored and humbled when my hometown of Chrudim presented me with an Award of Honorable Citizenship many years after I left there and had become a citizen of the United States.

Of course, I have known sadness as well. My mother's melancholy mood haunted my young life. Because she shielded me from the realities of the war going on around us, I was never able to comprehend the enormity of her burden. I was never able to achieve what I wanted most—to make her happy.

I've come to a place of peace with that. I realize she gave me so much else—her intellect, her matter-of-fact ways, and her compassion for others. If I've suffered in life, what has hurt me most is losing the ones I love. Loneliness is life's heaviest burden.

I have had the great fortune to love and be loved by good men. My husband Jarda worked hard his whole life to care for me and our daughter. He fought bravely his afflictions near the end of his life. My dear friend František epitomized the goodness in mankind. His art reflected his sensitivity, and he gave me great joy when my will to live was at its lowest. Both of these men were competent, gentle, and caring.

If I were asked by a young person how to find love, I would tell them this: work hard and be serious about what you do; be kind, gentle, and caring with all those you know; try to understand others even when you do not agree with them. If you do these things, love will find you.

But the young rarely ask the old such questions. To be free to live your own life means to be free to make your own mistakes.

Some cultures believe the ghosts of our ancestors live among us. They swoop down at night and inhabit our houses and our dreams. I believe our loved ones are always with us. I am engulfed in Jarda's presence. I walk in nature with my grandparents and my father beside me. I sit quietly and think about what to do next in life—sometimes in a melancholy mood—but constantly with my mother by my side. I lie in bed dreaming of love, and of making love—by the rivers and mountains in Czech lands—with a good and decent man.

Má vlast, můj život a moje láska
My country, my life, and my love

Index of Characters

The immediate Caslavsky family:
Vera Novak-Caslavsky, girl from Chrudim whose story is told.
Jaroslav (Jarda) Caslavsky her husband.
Veronika, their daughter.

The extended family:
Vilem Novak, Vera's father, a lawyer.
Vera Kudrnka-Novak, Vera's mother.
Grandpa Vilem Novak, Vera's paternal grandfather, a lawyer.
Grandma Ludmila (Lida) Novak, Vera's paternal grandmother.
Grandpa Eduard (Eda) Kudrnka, Vera's maternal grandfather, a physician
Grandma Barbora Kudrnka, Vera's maternal grandmother.
Eda Kudrnka, Vera's uncle, a physician.
Fanynka, Grandma Kudrnka's maid and Vera's nanny
Aunt Eva, Vera's father's older sister in Liberec
Grandma Caslavsky, Jarda's mother in Týniště
Hana, Jarda's sister in Týniště
František, Vera's precious friend from the Czech Republic.

People who helped along the way:
Opa and Hilda Leitner, Vera's father's best friend and his wife
Mr. Šada, Vera's High School teacher
Mr. V—, Jarda's Sokol brother
Ms. K—, Official at Police headquarter who granted them travel permission.
Anneliese & Rudi, friends of Vera's mother in Vienna

Mrs. Juranek, kind woman in Vienna

Dr. Megla, Director of Corning glass research facility in Raleigh, NC

Erich & Lotte Christian and their daughter Elizabeth, kind family in Raleigh

Dr. Rustom Roy, from the Materials Research lab at Penn State

Helene, Dr. Roy's secretary at Penn State

Don Strickler, Vera's Grad Student colleague at Penn State.

Mr. D—, FBI Agent in Pennsylvania

Mr. Cattell, Penn State administrator

Joseph Clark Jr, Senator from Pennsylvania

Joe & Bubbles Gallo & their 3 children, surrogate family related to Vera's cousin

Dr. Newnham, bridge partner from the Penn State lab

Ilsa Mahler, daughter of friend of Opa's in Germany.

Oscar Rodan and his sister Alice Wagner, old family friends

Tian-jia, Chinese exchange student at the Forsyth institute

Vera and Jarda at their 50th Wedding
Anniversary

Church of St. Bartholomew the Apostle in Koçi, 4 miles east of Chrudim, where Grandpa Kudrnka was baptized and married.

Chrudim Town Square

The Church of the Assumption of the Virgin Mary in Chrudim, where Vera was baptized and married.

Grandpa Kudrnka's house at 54 Palackeho Ulice (street) where Vera was born. The bottom floor was his medical office and apartment. The top floor was Vera's parents' apartment.

Vera at 10 years old

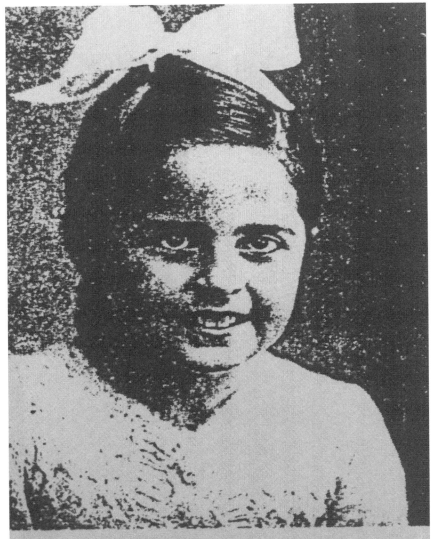

In 1944, when I was ten years old .

New York Daily Mirror June 11, 1948. 10
Thousand Czech's seek refuge from
Communist control.

the convictions to date represented only a fraction of the "goug-
ing racket."
Koenig said he will appeal.

, but
con-
ip to
cided
roba-
lost
ven-

o go
1 ad-
He
mann

ities
than
have
the
hich
pros-
ney.
itage
peo-
"

"sad
Green-
work
$9,000

House May Vote To Admit Czechs

WASHINGTON, June 10 (UP).
—The House today tentatively
adopted an amendment to its dis-
placed persons bill calling for
the admission to this country of
Czechs who fled from their homeland after the Communists gained
control.

It was introduced by Rep.
Stefan (R.-Neb.), who said the
State Department reported that
not more than 2,000 of the 10,000
to 12,000 Czechs who have sought
refuge in the western zones of
Germany and Austria, would
seek admission to the U. S.

House Republican leaders de-
layed a final vote on the bill
until tomorrow.

Engine Trouble Halts Ship

SOUTHAMPTON, England,
June 10 (UP).—The steamer

scars.
"One:
low a s
inch sca
eration.
"Two:
large d
three in
"Three
margin
left by
growth.
"Four
able 'scr
long, on
dish-pur
plastic s
The te
set earlie
nered Ba
statement
"No, I
usual sc
Opposi
defendan
years re
ranks of
contended
normal h
He also
that he i
himself t
fortune,

ART
II
1948

Josefa Ressela Gymnázium - Vera's High School

Jarda as a young man with his sister Hana
and their parents.

Vera and Jarda at their state marriage in Prague. They were later married at her church in Chrudim.

Baby Veronika and Vera

Grandma Kudrnka and Baby Veronika

Fanynka and Baby Veronika

Veronika at 4 years old on the Beach in Bulgaria. Regular seaside vacations were part of the escape plan.

Veronika at 8 years old when she was left
with Grandma Caslavsky in Týniště.

Veronika with her cousin Jirka growing up in Týniště.

Vera's Passport Photo when she came to
America

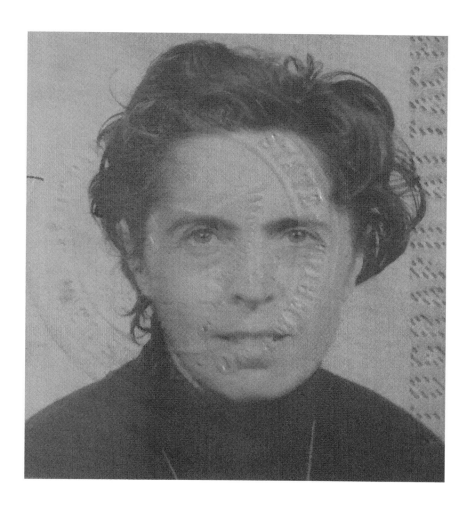

Vera's PhD from Charles University. (Soviets mandated the socialist title of Candidate vs. the capitalist title of PhD.)

Universita Karlova

ROZHODNUTÍM VĚDECKÉ RADY
ZE DNE 1. DUBNA 1965   ČÍS. PROTOKOLU 1324

PODLE § 3 ZÁKONA
Č. 53 ZE DNE 26. ÚNORA 1964

U D Ě L I L A

Věře čáslavské, prom. chem.
NAR. DNE 18. LEDNA 1934   V CHRUDIMI

VĚDECKOU HODNOST KANDIDÁTA

CHEMICKÝCH VĚD

Jarda's PhD from Penn State

THE PENNSYLVANIA STATE UNIVERSITY

BY AUTHORITY OF THE BOARD OF TRUSTEES AND UPON
THE RECOMMENDATION OF THE FACULTY OF THE GRADUATE SCHOOL
AND OF THE SENATE HEREBY CONFERS UPON

JAROSLAV · LADISLAV · CASLAVSKY

THE DEGREE OF

DOCTOR · OF · PHILOSOPHY

IN RECOGNITION OF THE COMPLETION OF ADVANCED STUDY IN

GEOCHEMISTRY

IN TESTIMONY WHEREOF THE UNDERSIGNED HAVE SUBSCRIBED
THEIR NAMES AND AFFIXED THE SEAL OF THE UNIVERSITY THIS
FOURTEENTH DAY OF JUNE 1969

PRESIDENT OF THE BOARD OF TRUSTEES

Eric A. Walker
PRESIDENT OF THE UNIVERSITY

M. Nelson McGeary
DEAN OF THE GRADUATE SCHOOL

Vera at 38 and Veronika at 15 returning from
Germany

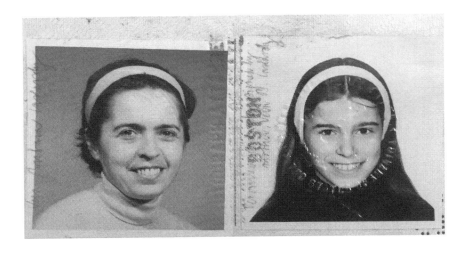

Veronika in College

Veronika as wife and mother.

Veronika and her children.

Vera and Jarda retire to Florida in 1993.

Jaroslav Caslavsky 1929–2012.

Krkonoše where Jarda skied and where his ashes were spread.

"Eternal Spring" Art Photo of Jarda done by Vera.

František

František Art

Vera and František in the Alps.

A Word about Czech Forms

Pronunciation

Diacritical marks over letters, such as the *caron* over *č* and the *acute* over *á*, change the sound-values of the letters to which they are added. The *č*-sound softens to *ch* and the *á*-sound is held longer than a plain *a*. Thus, the name *Čáslavská* is pronounced *Chaas-lav-skaa*, where the double a indicates the *a*-sound is held longer, *Dubček* becomes *Dub-chek*, and *Šada* becomes *Shada*.

Female Surnames

Many last names of female family members end with the suffix —*ová* or —*á*. Thus, the family names *Novák* and *Kudrnka* become *Nováková* and *Kudrnkovà* to indicate a female member of the family.

In this book, for simplicity sake, I omit the diacritical marks (except in the cases of historical figures whose names are more recognizable with the marks), and I stick to the English language custom of using the same last name for male and female members of a family. However, to pay homage to the Czech heritage of the main characters, I list their names in the forms they would use:

English Form / Czech Form

Vera Novak Caslavsky / Věra Nováková-Čáslavská
Jaroslav (Jarda) Caslavsky / Jaroslav (Jarda) Čáslavský
Vilem Novak / Vilém Novák

Vera Kudrnka-Novak / Věra Kudrnková-Nováková
Grandpa Vilem Novak / Grandpa Vilém Novák
Grandma Ludmila (Lida) Novak / Grandma Lida Nováková
Grandma Barbora Kudrnka / Grandma Barbora Kudrnková
Grandma Caslavsky / Grandma Čáslavská

Acknowledgments

My thanks to Vera Caslavsky. She was generous with her time, her personal records, and her family photos. I also want to acknowledge her daughter Veronika for her help in pinning down the times of events that had escaped her mother's memory. Vera spent many hours helping me to understand the Czech experience, but it was through the actions of her, Veronika, Jarda, who I met in his declining years, and František that I came to know the Czech heart. Without that, this book would not have been possible.

I must also acknowledge my author-daughter, Robin, who encouraged me to make writing a second career. My appreciation extends to both Grub Street in Boston and the Fine Arts Work Center in Provincetown where I got to practice my craft. A special shout out goes to my South Florida editor and mentor Virginia Aronson. Lastly, my gratitude to my wife, Anne, who serves ably as muse and mate.

Citations for Photos & Art

Chrudim Town Square

User: Harold, *"Resselovo náměstí, Chrudim, Chrudim District, Czech Republic."* WikiMedia Commons, July 1, 2018, https://www.commons.wikimedia.org

The Church of the Assumption

Autor:Zp, *"Archdecanal church of Assumption in Chrudim, Czech Republic."* WikiMedia Commons, March 7, 2006, https://commons.wikimedia.org

Josefa Ressela *Gymnázium*

Ben Skála, "Chrudim-gymnázium2013c." WikiMedia Commons, April 26, 2013, http://commons.wikimedia.org

Map

Electionworld & Shazz, "Maps of Czechoslovakia in 1928-1938 with marked borders of all four Czechoslovak lands and their regional capital cities." WikiMedia Commons, August 12, 2011, http://commons.wikimedia.org

About the Author

JK DeRosa writes fiction and nonfiction. His work has been published in journals and short story anthologies. He splits his time between Cape Cod and South Florida.

Printed in Great Britain
by Amazon

43640577R00135